VOLUME 14

◁ **COVER PHOTOGRAPH**
Peafowl. (Page 1679)
The beauty of the shimmering plumage of the male offsets its screeching voice. Here the male peacock displays its glorious colours; the peahen is less showy and has no train.

FRONTISPIECE ▷
Panda. (Page 1648)
Chinese mother love. The baby shown here was born at the Peking zoo. Two pandas, Hsing-hsing and Ling-ling, were presented to the Washington, D.C. zoo recently by the Chinese government.

FUNK & WAGNALLS WILDLIFE ENCYCLOPEDIA

GENERAL EDITORS • Dr. Maurice Burton and Robert Burton

Also published as The International Wildlife Encyclopedia and Encyclopedia of Animal Life.
Funk & Wagnalls, Inc., New York, New York

Ovenbird

The large family of South American ovenbirds are named after the clay nests that some species make. The 220-odd species are divided into several groups of diverse forms: the 'true ovenbirds' of the genus **Furnarius,** *the spinetails, thornbills, earth-creepers, shaketails, foliage-gleaners, leafscrapers, castlebuilders and many others with equally bizarre names.*

Most of the family have dull brown plumage with shades of rufous or chestnut and vary in length from 5–11 in. The spinetails have brighter plumage than most ovenbirds and the pale-breasted spine-tail has bright yellow and black on its chin. The 8in.-long rufous ovenbird, or **el hornero,** *the barber, is bright chestnut above and whitish below. Although the plumage is generally drab and uninteresting there is some variety in form. The spinetails have very long, sometimes forked, tails. That of Des Mur's spinetail is two or three times as long as the rest of the bird and in some the webs of the tailfeathers have become reduced so the central quill projects. A few species have crests and* **Xenops minutus** *has an unusual upturned, wedge-shaped bill.*

Ovenbirds range from southern Mexico to Patagonia but the largest number of different forms are found in the Argentinian pampas and mountainous regions of Chile. In North America there is an ovenbird **Seiurus aurocapillus** *which builds an oven-shaped nest of grass but belongs to the wood warbler group.*

Wide range of habits

Surprisingly little is known about the habits of this widespread, diverse and numerous family. It has been said that the reason why so little is known about South American birds compared with African birds is that in Africa the birds were studied by the keen amateur ornithologists among the British colonial administrators. With a few notable exceptions, there have been few comparable studies made of South American birds

and our knowledge of many ovenbirds is limited almost entirely to name and plumage. This is regrettable because the members of the family have taken up an enormous range of habits and habitats, on a scale comparable at least with the icterids (see oropendola, p 1632).

• Ovenbirds are shy and because of their unassuming plumage tend to be overlooked. The rufous ovenbirds are among the most conspicuous because their domed clay nests are a feature of the open country in Argentina and neighbouring states where they can be seen on trees, fence posts and sometimes on the eaves of houses. The habits of rufous ovenbirds are rather like those of larks and thrushes that feed on the ground. The miners and earth-creepers are also terrestrial and some species prefer to run rather than fly when disturbed. The shaketails can be found along water-courses, continually flicking their tails like their aquatic counterparts the wagtails. Some of the shaketails are even found along the shores of Chile where they feed among the floating kelp, so being the only passerine or perching birds to have taken on even a partially marine way of life. The sharp-tailed streamcreeper also lives by streams, preferring those with sewage effluent.

Other members of the family are marsh birds and many live in woods and forests. The treerunners have stiff tails which they use as props when climbing tree trunks, as do nuthatches and woodpeckers. The foliage-gleaners search for insects among the leaves, like warblers; while on the ground, among dense undergrowth, the leafscrapers search among fallen leaves, tossing them in the air rather like blackbirds do.

Similar diet

Despite their great range of habits, most ovenbirds eat insects, the kinds of insects eaten no doubt depending on the places where the ovenbirds live. The shaketails that forage among the kelp beds feed on small crustaceans and other marine animals and a few species feed on seeds.

Nesting not well-known

Ovenbirds have varied songs, ranging from the ringing cries of the miners to the harsh jay-like screams of the brown cachalote and the musical duets of the rufous ovenbirds.

Many ovenbirds either build solid nests out of clay or plants or nest in burrows, with the result that very little is known about their breeding habits. The eggs, 3–5 in number, are usually white. Incubation lasts in studied species for 15–20 days and the chicks fledge in 13–18 days.

Many palaces

Studying the nesting habits of ovenbirds is difficult because many of them make nests whose contents cannot be examined without destroying them. The rufous ovenbird makes its nest of clay strengthened with grass, building up the walls until they are 1½ in. thick. The nest is built in the winter when the rains make the clay soft enough to work. The pair first build a cup then continue adding to the walls until the nest is roofed in. The nesting chamber which is lined with grass is reached by a curved corridor. The nest is sufficiently strong to last 2–3 years before being washed away by the rains, but the ovenbirds build new nests each year. After the nests have been abandoned they are taken over by hornets, wasps, and birds such as swallows and cowbirds.

The miners and earthcreepers live in burrows, digging their own or using natural cavities and burrows of viscachas. Other ovenbirds build large structures in trees. The firewood-gatherer makes a huge structure of sticks and the white-throated cachalote makes a nest strong enough for a man to stand on. The castlebuilders make their nests at the end of low branches, sometimes so heavy the branches bend to the ground.

class	**Aves**
order	**Passeriformes**
family	**Furnariidae**
genera & species	**Anumbius annumbi** *firewood-gatherer* **Furnarius rufus** *rufous ovenbird* **Geositta cunicularia** *common miner* **Pseudoseisura lophotes** *brown cachalote* **Sylviorthorhynchus desmursii** *Des Mur's spinetail* *others*

▽ *Rufous ovenbird, owner of the clay ovens found all over open country.*

▽ *Clay oven. These nests are built in the winter when the clay is soft.*

Wolfgang Lummer

J Allan Cash

Owlet moth

The setaceous Hebrew character, the true lover's knot, the beautiful yellow underwing and Mother Shipton, these are 4 of the 300 species of owlet moths living in Britain. In all there are over 6 000 species belonging to the family Noctuidae. As the common and scientific names suggest, most of them fly at night and are often seen gathering at artificial light.

Not surprisingly, there is great variation within this large family. Owlet moths range in size from a tropical American species with a 1 ft wingspan to the smallest species with a span less than $\frac{1}{3}$ in. Most owlets are dull coloured and difficult to see when they are resting on a leaf or tree trunk. Many have patterning, called disruptive colouring, which helps to break up the outline of the body. Others, especially those living in the tropics, have gaudy colours, and some of the drab owlets have brilliantly coloured hindwings which are hidden under the forewings when the moths are at rest. When disturbed the wings are spread and the colours suddenly appear. This is called 'flash coloration' and is presumed to be a means of defence—startling a predator sufficiently to allow the moth to escape. Owlet moths that have coloured rear wings are often called underwings.

A particular feature of owlet moths, and of some other families, are the 'ears' or tympanic organs situated on the thorax The latter name is preferable, because although they are hearing organs, their mechanism is different from that of vertebrate ears. The tympanic organs, one each side of the body, consist of a cavity that is covered by a stretched membrane, or tympanum.

Night fliers

Most noctuid moths hide during the day in crevices or rest on the bark of tree trunks where they usually remain unseen because of their camouflage. A large number are, however, abroad by day and can be seen on flowers in the company of butterflies and bees. Some of these owlets live in Arctic regions where there is continuous daylight during the summer. The night fliers come out at dusk when, like their daytime relatives, they can be seen feeding at flowers. Owlet moths have a long proboscis or tongue with which they suck nectar from flowers or sip fruit juices and sap.

A few owlet moths migrate, often in vast numbers. The cotton moth of America, a serious pest of cotton, migrates north in the autumn, coming to rest 1 000 miles or more north of the cotton belt and consequently dies without breeding. It is so abundant in the warmer cotton-growing areas, however, that each year there is a surplus which flies north. The silver Y, named after the patterns on its wings, flies from Africa, across the Mediterranean and into Europe during the spring. Unlike

△ **Miselia** just emerging from the minute eggs.

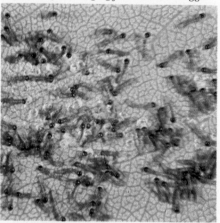
△ Newly hatched **Miselia** caterpillars.

△ **Plusia chalcytes** caterpillar moves in loops.

△ **Plusia gamma** with its disruptive colouring.

the cotton moth, the silver Y breeds in the northern parts of its range but it does not survive the winter.

Say it with scent

For some years it has been known that moths of many species use scent to attract one sex to the other. The sensitivity of the scent organs in the antennae is remarkable and a single female can attract males from considerable distances. Male owlets can often be distinguished by their feathery antennae on which there are many organs of smell.

The scent is disseminated by structures called brushes. Owlet moths have a pair of brushes which lie in pockets on the back of the abdomen. When at rest the lips of the pockets are tightly closed so that the scent is kept in. The brushes look like widely-splayed camel hair paint brushes and while lying in their pockets they are charged with the scent chemical that is secreted from special glands. Then, when a female owlet moth is ready to mate the brushes are lifted out of their pockets and the scent is blown away by the wind.

The courtship of the angle shades moth, which resembles a shrivelled leaf, has been studied in the laboratory. Mating takes place at dawn, the males remaining at rest until the females expose their brushes. They then fly up wind to the females and on reaching them evert their own brushes for a second or two before proceeding to mate. The males' scent can sometimes be detected by the human nose and in the angle shades moth it has been identified as being mainly a simple chemical called benzaldehyde. It is thought that its function is to inform the female of the species of the male so she does not allow the wrong species to mate with her, and to stimulate her into breeding condition.

The eggs are laid on or near the particular plants on which the caterpillars will feed. Some owlet caterpillars, such as the bollworm (p 256), are pests of crops. The caterpillar pests are sometimes called cutworms or army worms. The latter name is given when vast masses of caterpillars exhaust one supply of food and migrate in search of another.

The caterpillars usually feed at night, lying up by day in crevices or in bunches of leaves that are fastened together with silk. The pupae are usually formed in crevices in the ground.

Ultrasonic tactics

Bats are the main enemies of owlets and other moths that fly by night. It is now well known that bats search for and track down their prey by echo-location or sonar. The sonar system has been shown to be very sensitive and it would seem that bats ought to have no difficulty in catching their prey. Recent experiments have, however, shown that owlet and other moths, as well as lacewings, take avoiding action. The tympanic organs of owlet moths are sensitive to the ultrasonic squeaks of bats. A moth has an advantage because it can hear the bat's squeaks from some distance but the bat has to come quite close to the moth before it can hear the very faint echoes returning from it. When a moth hears a bat it turns and flies in the opposite direction and, with luck, it keeps far enough away to prevent the bat detecting it. The bat makes this difficult by continually changing direction so the moth is confused as to which direction it should flee. If the bat does get so close that its squeaks are so loud the moth cannot tell from which way they are coming, the moth drops to the ground and hides.

phylum	**Arthropoda**
class	**Insecta**
order	**Lepidoptera**
family	**Noctuidae**
genera & species	**Alabama argillacea** *cotton moth* **Amathes c-nigrum** *setaceous Hebrew character* **Anarta myrtilli** *beautiful yellow underwing* **Euclidimera mi** *Mother Shipton* **Lycophotia varia** *true lover's knot* **Phlogophora meticulosa** *angle shades* **Plusia gamma** *silver Y* *others*

△ *Dead or alive? An angle shades moth excellently camouflaged amongst dead leaves.*

▽ *A glistening herald **Scoliopteryx libatrix**, a noctuid moth, hibernating in a damp mine.*

R Skiba: Bavaria

Owlet-nightjar

This bird is known by a variety of names such as moth owl, fairy owl and, in particular, owlet-frogmouth. Owlet-nightjar is the name now most favoured in Australia. It is neither an owl nor a nightjar or frogmouth but it is superficially like these birds and belongs to the same family as the nightjars and frogmouths. An owlet-nightjar looks rather like a little owl, having a rounded head and weaker, shorter bill than is usual in other members of the family. Its posture when perched is almost as upright as an owl's, but the tail is fairly long with rounded feathers. The smallest species is about 6 in. long and the largest no more than 1 ft. The plumage is dark brown on the back, lighter on the front with patterns like those in an owl's plumage. A notable feature is the tufts of hairy feathers, with separated barbs, that stick up from the forehead and chin.

The seven species of owlet-nightjars differ little in appearance. Five live in New Guinea, one of which also lives in many parts of Australia and Tasmania. One species lives in the Moluccas and another in New Caledonia.

Direct flight

Owlet-nightjars are nocturnal, usually being seen at twilight, but occasionally during the day when the sky is overcast. As a result they are as elusive as nightjars and little is known of their habits. They live in wooded country, hiding during the day in hollow branches or in dense foliage, but some species can be found in grassland. Their flight is more direct than that of nightjars and frogmouths and they perch on branches in the normal crosswise position rather than lengthwise like other members of the family. They eat insects which they sometimes catch on the wing but most of their food, beetles being particularly favoured, is obtained from the ground. Thus their feeding habits are intermediate between the aerial hawking of nightjars and the ground feeding of frogmouths.

Two broods a year

Nothing is known of the courtship of owlet-nightjars which is not surprising considering their nocturnal woodland habits. The eggs are laid in the same hollow branches that the birds roost in but are also laid in tunnels in banks. Sometimes the hollow is lined with green leaves or fur but it is more usual for it to be left bare. The eggs, 3 or 4 in number, are white, sometimes spotted, and almost spherical, nearly 1 in. in diameter. The incubation period and details of care of the brood are not known, except that both parents play a part. The young hatch with a covering of dense white down. In Australia, and presumably elsewhere, two broods are raised each year.

▷ *Owlet-nightjars* Aegotheles cristata *in their typical poses: one sitting on the end of a tree stump, and one perched crosswise.*

Easily flushed

Although not active during the day owlet-nightjars can be heard calling from their hollows. The call is a double churring note or a whistle. The exact location of the owlet-nightjar can be found by rapping the trunks of trees; if there is an owlet-nightjar inside it peers out, owl-like, and hisses at the intruder. If disturbed further, the owlet-nightjar flies direct to another branch where it perches facing the source of disturbance. This seems unnecessary as it can turn its head through 180°.

class	**Aves**
order	**Caprimulgiformes**
family	**Aegothelidae**
genera & species	***Aegotheles albertisi*** ***A. cristata,*** *others*

J Robert: Jacana

Oxpecker

Oxpeckers, or tick birds, have a remarkable natural history, as they spend most of their time in association with large mammals. They are often seen perching on the backs of African game, feeding on the ticks, blood-sucking flies and tissues of their hosts. Rhinoceros, giraffe, hippopotamus and eland are favourite big mammalian hosts but oxpeckers are often seen cleaning smaller ones such as impala. The association is mutual: the oxpeckers feed, the mammals have their pests removed and are also warned of danger by the alarm calls of the birds. So dependent are the oxpeckers on this relationship that there is little of their life that is not linked with it. Even their claws are adapted to this, being curved and very sharp, for clutching the hide of the host. Their tails are stiff, like those of woodpeckers, to give support on a vertical surface such as the flanks of a large animal.

The two species of oxpecker are confined to Africa and are very similar in appearance. They are close relatives of starlings, and are about 9 in. long with short flattened bills and longish tails. The plumage is almost uniform brown and the two oxpeckers are best distinguished by their bill colour. The red-billed oxpecker has a completely red bill, but the yellow-billed oxpecker has a yellow bill with a red tip. In flight it can be distinguished by a paler rump.

The yellow-billed oxpecker ranges from Senegal in the west to Ethiopia in the east, and Natal in the south; the red-billed is found only on the eastern side of the continent. The ranges of the two overlap and at times both can be seen perching on the same animal. It is most unusual for two so closely related animals to live in the same habitat and to have, apparently, the same feeding habits.

Becoming rarer

There may be a dozen or many more oxpeckers on one animal, perched in a line on its head or along its back, or running about over its body. Their sharp claws enable them to cling firmly while their host is galloping at full speed or to clamber under the belly and up and down the legs with the ease of a woodpecker or nuthatch on a tree trunk. Although the hosts seldom object to oxpeckers, they sometimes attempt to drive the oxpeckers away by flicking their tails or rolling on the ground, especially if they have open sores or wounds.

At one time oxpeckers could be found almost wherever there was wild game or cattle, but their range has diminished considerably as the game has been killed and domestic stock has been subjected to dipping. The poisonous dips kill the ticks, which are one of the oxpeckers' main

◁ *Hangers-on. Two yellow-billed oxpeckers take a drink, clinging to the neck of a roan antelope.*

1617

sources of food, and probably kill the ox-peckers which eat the poisoned ticks. Ox-peckers have disappeared entirely from some areas. Some farmers, both African and European, have not regretted the dis-appearance of the oxpeckers because of the damage they do to hides by enlarging wounds and aggravating sores. It is also claimed, without evidence, that oxpeckers spread diseases such as rinderpest. In fact, they are more likely to be beneficial because they eat the blood-sucking flies which are known to be carriers of disease. Some cattle-farming tribes, such as the Fulani of Gambia and Masai of Kenya, realising this, encourage oxpeckers.

Blood drinkers

Oxpeckers occasionally eat carrion but their main diet is insects plucked from the host's back or caught as they fly near the host. Ticks and flies make up the greatest num-ber of insects taken but some lice, as well as mites, are also eaten. Pieces of flesh are cut out of sores and wounds, which are also kept clear of maggots. Oxpeckers remove ticks and pieces of skin by a 'scissoring' action of the flattened bill, which is laid sideways on the skin. They drink the mois-ture from around their hosts' eyes and also blood. It appears that the blood the ticks have gorged is more important to the ox-peckers than the tissues of the ticks them-selves. In a series of altruistic experiments, Derek Goodwin demonstrated the ox-peckers' fondness for blood by presenting a cut finger to a captive oxpecker which immediately pecked at it.

Hair-lined nests

The oxpeckers' hosts provide more than food. The birds regularly sunbathe on the warm backs of the big animals and they also mate there. Breeding takes place during the rainy season. The nest is built in a hole in a tree or in a rock, or sometimes in the eaves

△ *A red-billed oxpecker, using its tail for support, pauses at its nest entrance before it disgorges a beakful of ticks to its young.*

▽ *One satisfied customer, a cow has its ear deloused by a red-billed oxpecker. Many animals welcome the attention of these birds.*

Peter Johnson

AS Cheke

of a house or amongst thatch. It is made from dry grasses and is lined with a pad of hair plucked from the mammals' backs. The clutch consists of three, sometimes as many as five, eggs.

Oxpeckers' favourites

Recent observations show that oxpeckers do not choose their hosts at random, nor do they merely settle on the animals with the most ticks. There is good evidence that they will keep returning to a particular animal in a herd, sometimes even when it has died. On one occasion a group of oxpeckers settled on a particular hippopotamus in a herd every time it surfaced, and another group visited a dead Cape buffalo for 2 days after it had been shot. Some species of big game are preferred as hosts, but the preference varies from place to place. Oxpeckers are very rarely seen on elephants and this seems to be because elephants will not tolerate them. On the other hand rhinoceroses are very common hosts.

Oxpeckers have always been unpopular with hunters because their alarm calls alert their hosts. This is apparently not just a matter of the hosts learning to associate the oxpeckers' calls with danger. There have been instances of oxpeckers deliberately trying to alert their hosts. They fly around their heads calling and when an exhausted young rhinoceros failed to react to the warnings, the oxpecker flew low over its head calling repeatedly until the rhinoceros eventually got up.

class	**Aves**
order	**Passeriformes**
family	**Sturnidae**
genus & species	***Buphagus africanus*** *yellow-billed oxpecker* ***B. erythrorhynchus*** *red-billed oxpecker*

Atlas/Dragesco : Bavaria

Popperfoto

△ *Oxpeckers on their feeding grounds—a zebra proves a better bet than a roan antelope. One bird feeds upside down from the antelope's belly.*

▽ *The glassy orange eye and broad flashy bill brightens up the drab brown plumage of a yellow-billed oxpecker.*

Des Bartlett: Photo Res

Oyster

The true oyster of the family Ostreidae is the European flat oyster, **Ostrea edulis**. Its well-known shells are untidy and irregular in outline (often made more so by a variety of encrusting animals and plants growing on them) and there are such big local differences in appearance that with experience one can sometimes tell in which bed a particular oyster lived. The two valves are unlike, the right one being flat and the left convex. They are hinged in the pointed region of the 'beaks', held together by the triangular elastic ligament. There are no hinge teeth such as are found in many bivalves. On each valve a series of wavy ridges centres around the beak, marking former positions of the margin. Ill-defined ridges radiate from the beak of the left valve, while the other valve bears horny scales, which are less rigid than the rest of the shell, allowing the valves to make good contact around the edges when pulled together. Oysters are unusual for the soft porous chalky masses laid down within the substance of the shell. Often, also, in the convex valves of older oysters, there are chambers filled with sea water smelling of hydrogen sulphide. These chambers are the result of the mantle surface shrinking during life, and they get their smell from the putrefaction of organic matter.

Looking between the valves when they are agape, one sees just the edges of the mantle—the tissue that lines, and secretes, the inside of the shell. This thickened mantle edge has short sensory tentacles and a muscular fold that controls the flow of water. Opening the shell farther with a knife, one sees the large central adductor muscle that closes the valves against the pull of the hinge ligament. Arranged more than half way around this and the general body mass are two double crescentic gills.

The oyster family includes two other genera, **Pycnodonte** and **Crassostrea** (formerly **Gryphaea**). Amongst the latter are the American, Portuguese and Japanese oysters more of which are eaten than of the sweeter European flat oyster. The Portuguese oyster, **C. angulata**, introduced into France in 1868, has been relayed, during the last few years, to beds on the east coast of Britain, but it seldom breeds there. **Crassostrea** is easily distinguished from **Ostrea** since its shell is elongated rather than round, its left valve is more deeply convex and the muscle scars inside are deep purple. Apart from these true oysters, there are other bivalves bearing the name of 'oyster'. These include the tropical pearl oysters **Pinctada** which are closer to the mussels and are, like them, attached by byssus threads, the thorny oysters **Spondylus**, and the saddle oysters **Anomia** which live attached to rocks by thick calcified byssuses which pass straight through a notch in the lower valve.

△ Gourmet's delight, an oyster lies in its larger left valve, pinky white and glistening.

▽ This fine Japanese drawing reveals the complicated structure of the oyster's body.

Yves Lanceau: Jacana

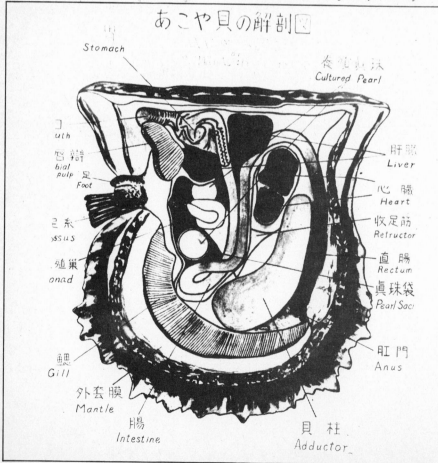

あこや貝の解剖図

Stomach

Cultured Pearl

コ
uth

貝瓣
bial
pulp
足
Foot

肝臓
Liver

心臓
Heart

收足筋
Retructor

足糸
yssus

殖巣
onad

直腸
Rectum

眞珠袋
Pearl Sac

鰓
Gill

肛門
Anus

外套膜
Mantle

腸
Intestine

貝柱
Adductor

J.Allan Cash

Several ways of feeding

The European flat oyster occurs down the Atlantic coast of Europe from Norway (latitude 65°) to Morocco and also in the Mediterranean and Black Sea. When it first settles as spat, it becomes attached by its convex left valve, but later it may become detached and turned over. The adult oyster then stays in one place, feeding by filtering small particles from the water. By beating the cilia on its complex, lattice-like gills, it draws a current of water in at a rate of perhaps 2 or 3 gallons an hour. The food particles, caught in mucous strings on these ciliated sieves, are wafted either to the bases or to the free edges of the gills and thence forwards to the mouth via the palps which sit either side of it and have a sorting function. Once in the digestive tract, the particles continue to be propelled by cilia to the elaborate ciliated stomach. It is in the stomachs of bivalves and of a few snails that there occurs perhaps the only truly rotating structure in the whole animal kingdom. This is the crystalline style, a rod of solid digestive enzymes, rotated by cilia in the sac that secretes it, dissolving at the tip where it rubs against a piece of cuticle, the gastric shield, and helping to wind in the strings of mucus in the manner of a windlass.

Not only does digestion take place in the cavity of the gut, but cells lining it also take in particles and digest them in their cytoplasm. Furthermore, some of the particles are engulfed by amoeba-like blood cells that come out into the gut cavity through the stomach walls and then migrate back with the food particles trapped in them.

At times the oyster is in danger of becoming clogged with sediment in its mantle cavity and at such times the valves are clapped shut which suddenly expels the water and sediment. This sudden 'cough' contrasts with the sustained closure of the shell in response to dangers from outside. The adductor muscle is in two parts, different to the naked eye as well as in microscopic structure. One part can contract rapidly; the other is able to remain contracted for long periods without tiring.

Sir or Madam

An oyster may change sex many times during its lifetime. This is not unusual amongst bivalves and the reproductive systems are so simple that the change involves little reorganisation. Maturing first as a male, the oyster takes some weeks to become a functional female but recovers his virility within a few days of discharging her eggs. In the cold waters off Norway, an oyster may change sex once a year, but in warmer waters, many times. Spawning occurs in summer when the temperature of the water exceeds about 15°C/60°F. The eggs pass through the gills against the water current and are fertilised in the mantle cavity by sperms carried in by the feeding current. They are not freed for about another 8 days. Then the shell is opened wide and closed violently at intervals, each time expelling clouds of larvae. Up to a million larvae may be incubated at a time, a large enough number, but small compared with the American oyster, *Crassostrea virginica*, which does not incubate its eggs but can release over a 100 million eggs at a time.

Peter Hill

△ *All valves shut tight, a bed of European flat oysters lies exposed on rocks at low tide.*

▽ *The highly convoluted shell with a fan-shaped base is the home of* **Ostrea gigas**.

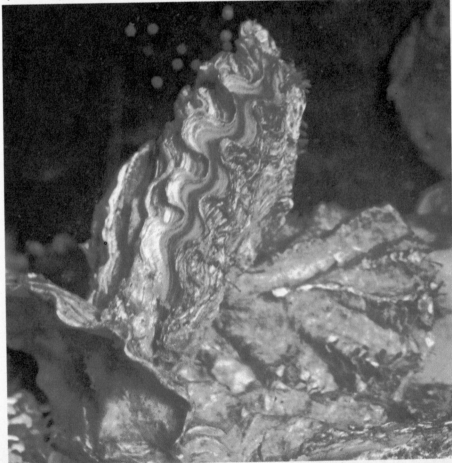

John Tashjian at Tacoma Aquarium

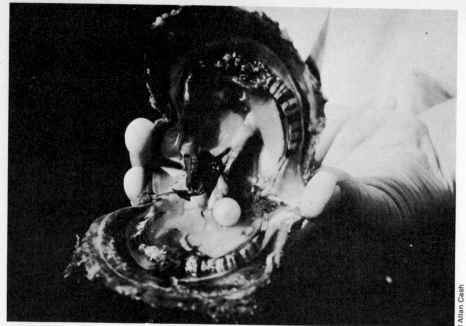

A large cultured pearl in **Pinctada partensi**, *formed by the oyster secreting pearly layers around a small piece of clam shell which is artificially introduced into its mantle.*

The eggs of the European flat oyster are about $\frac{1}{200}$ in. across and as they develop within the shell of the parent they change from white to black. At one time, 'whitesick' and 'blacksick' oysters were thought to be males and females respectively.

Explosive spawning
When released, the young, then known as a veliger larva, has a tiny shell with two adduc-

tor muscles, a ciliated tuft, or velum, for swimming and feeding, and a foot. For between 1 and $2\frac{1}{2}$ weeks the larva swims in the plankton, but when ready to settle, it protrudes its foot and grips any solid object it should touch. It then starts to crawl, but if the area is unsuitable, it can swim off again. Eventually, however, if it survives, the larva sticks itself down by its left valve using a drop of cement from the glands that in

Women pearl divers work before an enthusiastic audience at Toba. Japan supplies 99% of the world's cultured pearls, known to the Japanese as the 'tears of the moon'.

other bivalves secrete the byssus threads. At this stage, the oysters, about $\frac{1}{25}$ in. across, are known as spat. Now the shell grows rapidly and the body changes dramatically; foot, velum and eyes are lost, together with the anterior adductor muscles, the gill is increased and the mouth moves around through a right angle to the adult position.

It is important that males and females should spawn at the same time and to some extent this is aided by the dependence of spawning on temperature. In *Crassostrea* at least, however, chemical stimulation is also important. The sperms carry a hormone-like substance that stimulates spawning in both sexes and the males are also stimulated to spawn by the presence of eggs and by various organic compounds, including one present in seaweed. Thus one spawning individual can cause the whole population to release their eggs and spawn.

Downfall of the native

Great mounds of shells in coastal regions all over the world testify to the importance of oysters in the diets of many prehistoric communities. In Brittany there are banks 15 yds high, 700 yds long and 300 yds wide, containing shells of oysters, scallops and mussels. The Romans delighted in oyster orgies and were sufficiently impressed by English oysters to export them to Rome. Pliny records that the first person to establish artificial beds was Sergius Orata. During much of the 18th and 19th centuries, British beds were the most productive in Europe and vast quantities of this poor man's food were eaten. Today that huge harvest has dwindled so much that few can afford the price of a dozen oysters. Also much of the harvest now consists of the inferior Portuguese oysters. The decline started through overfishing which totally wiped out certain natural beds such as that in the Firth of Forth. Pollution also helped in the decline. About 1880, the introduction of the slipper limpet, with imported American oysters, meant competition for food. The slipper limpet can occur in vast numbers — as many as 446 to a square yard has been recorded. Neglect of the beds during the First World War was followed by a great mortality due perhaps to a parasitic infection. The worst predator of the oyster, a snail called the American oyster drill, was first spotted here in 1920 and was joined during the Second World War by a barnacle *Elminius* from the Antipodes which competes for settling space. Then, in the winter of 1962/63 the sea off the east coast of Britain almost froze and all but wiped out the oyster industry there.

phylum	**Mollusca**
class	**Bivalvia**
subclass	**Lamellibranchia**
order	**Eulamellibranchia**
family	**Ostreidae**
genus & species	***Ostrea edulis*** *European flat oyster, others*

Oystercatcher

The oystercatchers are large waders that are found in many parts of the world. Some species have black and white plumage, hence the old name of 'sea-pie' but others are all black. The most widespread oystercatcher *Haematopus ostralagus* is found in Europe, the Canaries, South Africa, Asia, Australia, New Zealand and North and South America. It is largely black above with white underparts and has a long red bill and pink legs. Another pied oystercatcher is the American oystercatcher *H. palliatus* that ranges from New Jersey and California to Argentina and Chile, while a third *H. leucopodus* lives in southern South America. The sooty oystercatcher *H. fuliginosus* lives on the coast of Australia and other black oystercatchers *H. bachmani* and *H. ater* live in western North America, southern South America and Australia. In some places the common oystercatcher is all black, as in the Canaries, Africa and America.

Moving inland

Oystercatchers are usually seen on rocky shores or sandy beaches, on mudflats, or in sand dune areas just behind the shore but they sometimes breed inland. They have nested inland in Scotland for centuries and they are now breeding inland in northern England. In New Zealand, oystercatchers are found by the snow rivers of South Island. Outside the breeding season oystercatchers gather in large flocks, and those that breed in high latitudes migrate to warmer regions in the winter. The Burry Inlet in South Wales, for instance, is the winter home of oystercatchers from Scotland, Iceland, the Faeroes and Norway.

The pied plumage and red bill of the oystercatcher are unmistakable, yet, surprisingly, they are sometimes difficult to see if they are motionless. They often give away their presence by their loud shrill calls of 'kleep-kleep' or a shorter, rapid 'kic-kic'. Oystercatchers are wary and run rapidly or take flight when approached.

Musselcatchers

It is difficult to see how the oystercatcher got its name. The authoritative *Handbook of British Birds* does not include oysters in the diet of the oystercatcher, and it would be surprising if it did because oysters live below the lowtide mark and oystercatchers feed between the tides or on land. A better name would be the old local name of musselpecker. Mussels, together with limpets, cockles, winkles, crabs and worms, make up a large part of the oystercatchers' diet. Cockles and worms are found by probing the sand with their bills. They also eat insects, especially their larvae, some plant food and occasionally eggs of other birds. The composition of the diet depends on the animal life living in the oystercatchers' habitat; whether sandy or rocky shores, farmland and so on.

The methods by which oystercatchers eat molluscs that are protected by strong shells, have been studied in detail. Limpets are dealt a sharp blow with the tip of the bill. Small ones are dislodged and large ones are shifted so they can be levered off or holed. The oystercatcher can then insert its bill and tear the strong muscles that hold the limpet down. Two different ways are used for opening bivalve molluscs such as mussels and cockles. If the shellfish is covered with water and its valves, or shells, are agape, the oystercatcher stabs downward then levers and twists to sever the adductor muscle that closes the valves. These fall open and the flesh is rapidly pecked out. If the shellfish are exposed to the air and firmly closed the oystercatcher has to smash its way in. Examination of mussel shells that were the remains of oystercatcher meals, shows that they are regularly smashed on the bottom edge and tests have shown that this side of the shell is much weaker than the top edge even in large mussels. The oystercatcher carries a mussel or cockle to a patch of firm sand, places it with its ventral margin upwards, and starts to hammer it. If the shell falls over it is righted or if it sinks it is carried to a firmer patch. On average, five blows of the bill are needed to penetrate a mussel shell and the bill is then inserted to cut the adductor muscle and prise the two halves apart. Cockle shells are not attacked in any particular position as their shells are weaker than those of mussels. Small crabs are flipped onto their backs and killed with a stab through the brain. The shell is then prised off and the flesh cut out with the same scissoring movements that are used for eating other shellfish.

In some places, such as the Burry Inlet

Posed on a cliff top beside a clump of thrift before flying down to feed at the mussel beds between the tide lines below. The strong red bill for prising open mussels and the thick red legs add flashes of colour to the oystercatcher's stark black and white plumage.

E H Herbert: AFA

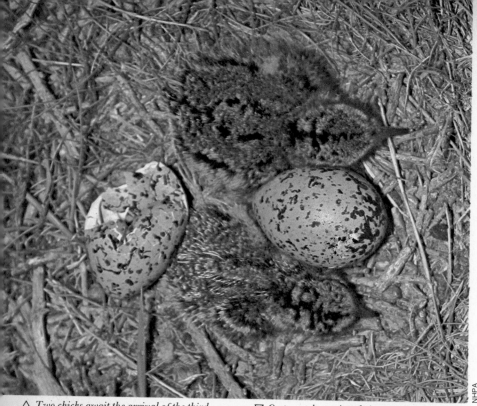

△ *Two chicks await the arrival of the third.*   ▽ *Oystercatchers wing their way along the shore.*

NHPA

in Britain, oystercatchers are considered a pest because of the damage they do to the cockle beds. Each oystercatcher eats about one cockle every minute and consumes on average 336 cockles per tide. As flocks number several thousands, they eat many millions of cockles each winter; but oystercatchers are only one of several enemies of cockles and it is debatable whether they seriously affect the cockle industry. In the Faeroes, where the oystercatcher is the national bird, they are considered beneficial as most of their food is insects and other invertebrates in grassland.

Piping display

Oystercatchers arrive at their breeding grounds in flocks but then split up into pairs. Each pair forms a territory which it defends against the other oystercatchers. Among their several displays there is the quite spectacular piping display in which a group of birds, or sometimes just a pair, run rapidly to and fro with necks outstretched and open bills pointing at the ground. At the same time they utter a piping call that varies from a clear 'kleep-kleep' to a quavering trill.

The nest is a shallow depression in shingle, sand or turf, sometimes with no lining but at other times lined with stones, shells, or dead plants. There are usually three eggs, yellowish or light brown with spots or streaks of dark brown. Both parents incubate the eggs which hatch in 24—27 days. The chicks leave the nest after a day or two and are fed by both parents. They fly in about 5 weeks and are fed by their parents for another 5 weeks.

Family traits

The careful study of the way oystercatchers open mussels was made by M Norton-Griffiths of Oxford University. He found that some oystercatchers regularly stabbed open mussels while others hammered the shells. Furthermore, young oystercatchers developed the same feeding habits as their parents. This is, perhaps, not so surprising as the chicks were learning to feed on only those animals which their parents brought to them. First the chicks practise pecking empty shells and picking up pieces of flesh left in them, learning the scissoring movements of the adults. Later they take opened shellfish from their parents and remove the flesh by themselves. Eventually they open the shells themselves, starting on small ones and graduating to large ones as they become more proficient. Norton-Griffiths never saw a 'crab-eating' chick attack a mussel and when a 'mussel-eating' chick found a crab it was frightened of it. The differences in feeding habits are so marked that a population of oystercatchers is distinctly divided by them and 'mussel-eaters' mate only with 'mussel-eaters' and 'cockle-eaters' with 'cockle-eaters'.

Fritz Siedel

class	**Aves**	
order	**Charadriiformes**	
family	**Haematopodidae**	
genus & species	*Haematopus ostralagus* oystercatcher, others	

▽ *S. African black oystercatcher* **Haematopus moquini**. △ *Oystercatchers on parade. Another regiment of waders feed alongside them in the background.*

Paca

The paca or spotted cavy is a large rodent found from Mexico to Brazil. In some places it is numerous, one report speaking of as many as 50 to an acre at times. It is stockily built, with a large broad head, and weighs up to 25 lb. It has a head and body length of 2½ ft, with only an inch of tail. The hindquarters are markedly higher than the shoulders. Its brown to black coat is made up of a soft underfur covered with coarse hair. There are usually 4 longitudinal rows of white spots on each side of the body, and the underparts are white to buff. It has large bulging eyes, moderate sized ears and the muzzle bears numbers of long whiskers. The short legs have 4 toes on each front foot and 5 on each hind foot.

The mountain paca is smaller and has a coat of soft thick fur. It lives in the forests of the Andes, at 6 000–10 000 ft, in a cold humid climate. Its muzzle is more slender than that of the lowland paca, its eyes less prominent, and it is believed to go into semi-hibernation in the cold season after it has stored fat in its body.

The pacarana or false paca **Dinomys branicki,** *similar in appearance to the paca and slightly larger, also lives in the mountain forests of the Andes. It belongs to another family, the Dinomyidae.*

Powerful diggers

Pacas usually live in swampy ground near a stream or river in the forest. They are strong swimmers and readily use water for escape when danger threatens. They spend the day in burrows which they dig using all four feet as well as their teeth which bite through large roots. Their large upper incisors will rip through thick plants. The burrows are 4–5 ft deep with two or more exits which are often plugged with leaves, but whether this is deliberate, or due to a natural accumulation of leaves because the exit has not been used for some time, is not known.

After dusk pacas leave their burrows singly and make their way to a feeding ground. They eat a variety of stems, roots, leaves and fallen fruit, especially avacados and mangos. When they get among crops of yam, cassava or sugar cane they can be destructive. A peculiarity of pacas is that they do not hold food in their forepaws when feeding, as the great majority of rodents do.

Reinforced cheek bones

The skull of the paca is unusual in having large cheek bones that enclose some of the jaw muscles. This condition is known in only one other rodent, the unrelated African maned rat *Lophiomys*. These large cheek bones form the outer walls of capacious cheek pouches and in old males may grow into enormous blister-like swellings, giving the head its grotesquely broad appearance. Another feature of the skull, not found in any other mammal, is that part of the cavity enclosed by the large cheek bone is specialised as a resonating chamber.

The eyes of the paca are large and bulging and its hearing and sense of smell are extremely acute. Although liable to become unduly fat with age, the paca is still very fleet of foot. The skin is said to be very thin and delicate so large strips may be ripped off during headlong rushes through spiky underground. Such wounds heal, however, in a remarkably short time.

Single births

There is normally a single young to a litter, although twins are born occasionally, and there are probably two litters a year. One paca in captivity in Rio de Janeiro had one young in February and another in July. The young is born in the underground burrow and is said at birth to be little larger than a mouse. It is not weaned for 2–3 months and takes several years to reach full size. A paca in captivity has lived to 16 years old.

Coveted tender flesh

Pacas are a prey to several carnivores and their flesh is prized by the local peoples, who hunt them with dogs. The carcases fetch high prices in the local markets. They are, however, rugged fighters if necessary and can deliver severe wounds with their teeth. When young or partly grown the paca is commonly exhibited in zoos, fairs and circuses, sometimes with the label 'what is it?' or 'the largest rat in the world'. Tourists to countries in which it lives usually meet it under these circumstances or in a

▽ *A paca contemplates its escape route. Although these solitary animals are terrestrial, they are good swimmers and usually make their escape in water. Their powerful clawed feet are used to dig burrows, their daytime homes, from which they emerge at night when their long whiskers are useful sense organs.*

Okapia

dish on their dinner tables under a variety of innocent or high-sounding names.

In spite of its aggressiveness a paca makes an amiable pet, and once tamed will follow its owner like a dog. Ivan T Sanderson has likened it to a walking garbage pail, an animal with an insatiable appetite that will eat almost anything and in large quantities.

One popular picture of a rodent is of a squirrel sitting on its haunches holding a nut in its paws; or it may be of a mouse doing the same. From this we get the idea that squirrels and mice pick up food with their forepaws. In fact, they pick up the food with their teeth, sit up on their haunches, hold up their forepaws and then drop the food into them from the mouth. The general run of rodents behave in the same way. There are, however, some rodents that use their forepaws as hands to pick up objects. A beaver, for example, will pick up a stick to gnaw the bark and the female will carry her babies in her paws. The coypu and the kangaroo rats also use their forepaws as hands when feeding. The paca is exceptional in not using them this way but the pacarana, which looks so much like it, does use its paws when feeding.

class	**Mammalia**
order	**Rodentia**
family	**Cuniculidae**
genus & species	***Cuniculus paca*** *paca* *C. taczanowskii mountain paca*

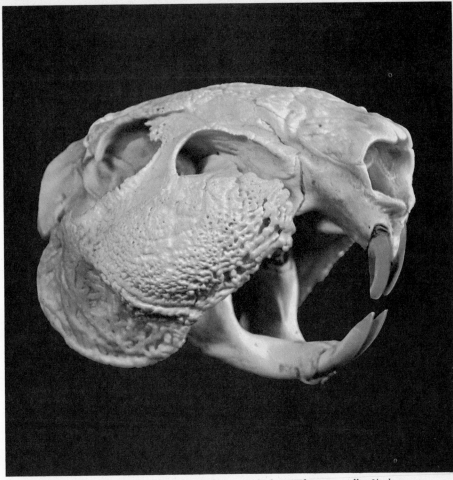

▽ *An impostor? The pacarana, or false paca, is larger and more thickset than the true paca.*

△ *Prominent cheeks. The large cheek bones of the paca, which form the outer walls of its huge cheek pouches, are very unusual as they enclose some of the jaw muscles.*

James Simon: Photo Res

Pacific salmon

There are six species of salmon in the North Pacific, by contrast with the North Atlantic where there is only one species, the Atlantic salmon (see p 100). Except for the Japanese species, the masu, these range from about Kamchatka in Siberia to the American west coast as far south as California. Of these the chinook, also known as the tyee, quinnat, king, spring, Sacramento or Columbia River salmon, weighs 10–50 lb, with a maximum of 108 lb. The sockeye, red or blueback salmon weighs 5–7 lb, but may weigh up to 15½ lb; the silver salmon or coho weighs 6–12 lb, going up to 26½ lb; the chum, keta or dog salmon weighs 8–18 lb; but is sometimes as much as 30 lb, and the humpback or pink salmon which is 3–5 lb, may weigh up to 10 lb.

Drastic changes for spawning

Pacific salmon return to spawn in the same river in which they hatched, and when they do so they become brilliant red, and their heads turn pea green. The males grow long hooked snouts and their mouths become filled with sharp teeth. The females do not grow the hooked snout. Most of the returning salmon are 4–5 years old. The humpback matures the earliest at 2 years, the silver salmon at 3, but some of the sockeye and chinook may be as much as 8 years old.

The salmon return in early summer, even in late spring, or in autumn in the case of the chum. They stop feeding as their digestive organs deteriorate and head for the coast from their feeding grounds out in the Pacific. On reaching the mouth of a river they head upstream, except the chum which usually spawns near tidal waters. The silver salmon moves only a short distance upstream. The chinook, on the other hand, has been known to travel as much as 2 250 miles up rivers. One exception to this is a subspecies of the sockeye which is non-migratory. In contrast with the Atlantic salmon, however, Pacific salmon never survive the spawning run.

Suicidal love-making

By the time the salmon near the spawning grounds, they are mere bags of bones housing the eggs or the sperms. The males often look the worse for wear as they fight with each other. The females look for a place in the sandy or gravelly shallows where the water is clear with plenty of oxygen. Then they start digging troughs (redds) in the river beds with their tails; each one lying on her side and flapping with her tail. When her trough is deep enough, she lies in it to spawn, her mate swimming over to her to shed his milt to fertilise the eggs. Each female lays several batches of eggs, to a total of 3–5 thousand, in different troughs, by the end of which time she is completely exhausted. With her tail fins worn to stubs, her skin blackening and with blotches of grey fungus attacking it, she dies. The males share the same fate, and the carcases of both drift downstream or are stranded at the edge.

Down to the sea as infants

Each batch of eggs becomes buried under sand as fresh redds are dug and the loosened sand is wafted over them. Thus protected, the orange-pink eggs hatch 8 weeks later. The alevins or young salmon remain under the gravel feeding on their yolk sacs for some weeks before wriggling to the surface as fry. They feed heavily on water fleas and other small animals and in the following spring are carried downstream by the current. The humpback and chum go to the sea as fry but the sockeye may go as fry or as 1–3 year fish, and the quinnat and coho go when 1–2 years old.

Finding their way home

There has always been a great interest in how salmon find their way back to the streams where they were hatched. The full story has not yet been pieced together but sufficient is now known to sketch in many of the details. There is evidence, for example, to show that the thyroid gland plays a part in the salmon's changing preference for water of varying salinity. When the coho was injected with a certain hormone it sought sea water. When the injections were stopped it sought fresh water. The opposite effect was found in the humpback. Probably other glands are involved, as well as the length of day and possibly the diet. The sense of smell may play a part, as it does in finding food. Temperatures also influence the fish, certainly once they have entered fresh water. When these are too low or too high the fish make no effort to surmount obstacles. There is some evidence also that celestial navigation, using the sun by day and the stars by night, as in migrating birds, keeps the salmon on their compass runs along the coast to the mouths of the rivers they came from.

Expert water-tasters

Of the different ways that salmon find their way back, one of the easier to test is the odour, or the taste of the water from which the fishes originated. Laboratory experiments have shown beyond doubt that fishes, including salmon, can recognize waters of only slightly different tastes; smell and taste are closely linked. This is not so very surprising since water-tasters dealing with the purification of drinking water are able to tell by tasting, in an almost uncanny way, where a particular glass of water came

▽ *Suffering from exposure: waste eggs trapped in stream debris. Eggs are usually covered by sand.* ▷ *Bursting with life. Spawning sockeye salmon.*

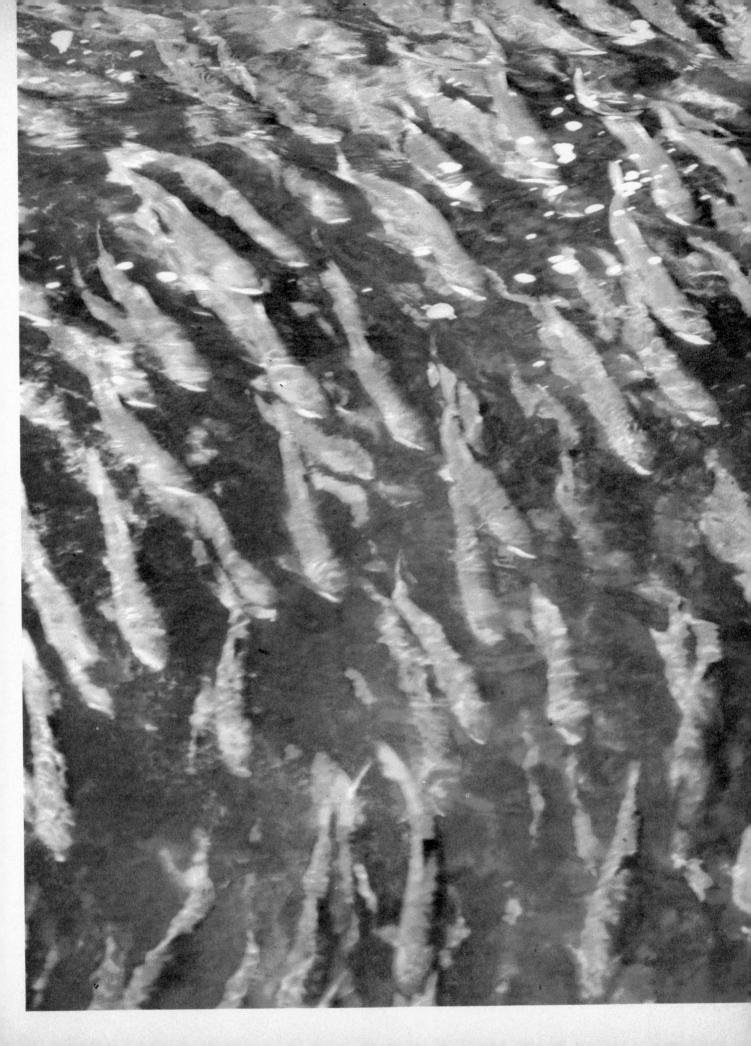

△ *On home ground. A pair of sockeye salmon, having swum from the Pacific Ocean up to the head waters of the river in which they hatched 4 or 5 years before, are now ready to spawn themselves — then die, starved and exhausted by their marathon journey on which they do not feed at all.*

from. These same tests show that the memory of a particular type of water persists for a long time in a fish, and that the younger the fish the longer the memory.

Controlled fishing

Many people living a long way from the Pacific are familiar with the Pacific salmon — in canned form. The salmon fishery is commercially highly valuable, with 2 – 10 million sockeye alone being caught and canned. The salmon are taken in gill nets, reef nets and purse seines on their way to the Fraser River in British Columbia. Unrestricted fishing could kill the industry,

so by an agreement between Canada and the United States, 20% of each race of fish are allowed through to continue their journey to the spawning grounds. This is taken care of by a joint International Pacific Salmon Fisheries Commission, which also arranges for the catch to be divided equally between the two countries. There is co-operation also in providing concrete and steel fishways to assist the salmon up the rivers. The Pacific salmon fishery is therefore as near as it has so far been possible to an actual husbandry of a wild resource. Moreover, research is being carried out to produce strains of salmon that can tolerate less favourable rivers than they

use at present, and to transplant fry which, when mature, will return to spawn in waters earmarked for cultivation.

class	**Pisces**
order	**Salmoniformes**
family	**Salmonidae**
genus & species	***Oncorhynchus gorbuscha*** *humpback*
	O. keta *chum*
	O. kisutch *silver salmon*
	O. masou *masu*
	O. nerka *sockeye*
	O. tshawytscha *chinook*

◁ *Caught on the run. A male salmon, caught on its way upstream to spawn, releases its milt under pressure from the teeth of a brown bear.*
▽ *The remains. Reduced to blackened bags of bones after spawning, dead sockeye salmon are washed up at the river's edge.*

△ *The many-roomed mansion of a pack rat.*
◁ *Pack rat portrait shows typical vole features including muzzle and small eyes.*

'▽ *Caught in the open: a dusky-footed wood rat. These shy creatures are rarely seen by day and when they do emerge they keep to shady places.*

Pack rat

Although called rats the pack rats, with their blunt muzzles, smallish eyes, fairly large ears and hairy tails, belong to the vole family. A packman was a pedlar who carried goods in a pack for sale. Pack rats have a similar reputation of 'bartering': when they take something, they always leave something in exchange. Their other names are trade rat and wood rat.

Pack rats are about 1½ ft long of which about half is tail and they weigh ¾ lb. They are dark brown to buff grey with white or buff underparts. In some species the hairs are sparse on the tail, but in others the tail is almost bushy.

The 22 species are found from British Columbia southwards to Nicaragua and throughout most of the United States. A typical species is the eastern or Florida pack rat. The bushy-tailed wood rat, 2 ft long, of which 8 in. is tail, ranges from British Columbia to California and eastward to the Dakotas. West of the Rockies is the dusky-footed wood rat which is the one that has been most studied.

Thief in the night
These nocturnal rats seem to have an insatiable habit of picking things up and hoarding them. If on the way to its nest a rat sees something more attractive it drops the object it is carrying and takes the new one. They collect and hoard all sorts of objects, especially bright or coloured objects, or those made of metal. Whatever they take, they tend to replace it with something else. Two of the more amusing examples concern miners' camps. In one was a box of metal nuts. When the time came to use the nuts the box was found filled with stones. In the other the rats stole worthless trinkets .from a prospector's cabin and left gold nuggets in their place — a good deal for the miners!

House builders
Some of the pack rats build houses of sticks with several 'rooms': some for storing food, others for sleeping, and one or more for their rubbish. The pack rats living in desert areas in the southwest United States, build their nests of pieces of cactus. They collect fragments of all kinds, including dead or living cactus and pile them against a living cactus, to a height of 2 ft and several yards across. Inside the heap is the nest, of dried grass and other soft materials,

and leading to it is a maze of passages protected by the hard sharp cactus spines, with just enough room for a rodent to squeeze through without impaling itself.

Cactus reservoirs
Pack rats live in woodlands, swamps, on rocky ground or in deserts. When near lakes or streams, although they do not enter water, they may build their nests over the water on or in fallen or leaning trees, and in mangrove swamps they build in the trees. They are mainly vegetarian, eating nuts, berries, leaves and roots, and a few small invertebrates. They drink little, getting their water from juicy plants. In deserts they get it almost entirely from the fleshy stems of cacti. Sometimes they live near farmhouses and then they can be a pest, not by their 'bartering' but by taking crops.

Handing over house to the children
Some pack rats are said to be monogamous, the male remaining with the female even when she has young. The male courts the female by drumming with his feet, this behaviour also being used as an alarm signal. In the northern parts of their range there may be one litter a year but in the southern parts there are two litters, and breeding

may occur throughout the year. Gestation is 33–39 days and there are 2–6 in a litter. The naked babies weigh ½ oz at birth. They begin to grow fur at 4 days and are fully furred in 2 weeks. They are weaned at 3 weeks, when the mother leaves her family to occupy the nest while she goes off to find or build a new one. Pack rats have the habit in common with a number of other rodents of licking saliva. The young lick the mother's saliva and possibly adults lick saliva as well. For the young it may be a way of transferring antibodies from mother to infant. In the adults it may have social significance, in promoting friendship and harmony. When two rats meet they stop a short distance from each other, sniff at each other's noses, then come close to lick each other's lips, mouth, face and head.

Another point of view

The species most extensively studied, the dusky-footed wood rat, does not seem to be monogamous. He mates with the female in the nearest nest but he is also a wanderer, going from one nest to another. The nest of this species is made of sticks. It has walls and a roof, usually two storeys, with passages and chambers. To an extent the nests are owned communally, in that the rats tend to swap houses much as we

do. When a male mates he continues to live with the female for a while. Once the female is pregnant, however, she drives the male out. Should he be reluctant to go she lunges at him furiously with her forefeet, striking forward and down, biting his ears, face, legs or breast—and he does not retaliate. The attack may prove fatal through suppuration of the wounds. Should a female attack a male near his own nest, however, it is quite a different story.

Ten years' hard labour

The differing opinions on whether or not the female tolerates the male reflects how little is known about animals, especially those small ones that move about at night. In 1951 two American zoologists, JM Linsdale and LP Tevis Jnr published their book, *The Dusky-footed Wood Rat*. Its 664 pages contained the results of 10 years' study of this one species. In spite of the information it contains the authors said that they still could not give a complete account of the rat's behaviour. One of their difficulties was that the rats usually came out only at night. If one came out during the day it sought the shady places. Even on moonlit nights the rats would stay at home, and an electric torch always made

△ *House bound. A dusky-footed wood rat asleep for the day. Its large house, with several rooms in the wild, is usually so placed as to be quite inaccessible to other animals.*

them scamper for shelter. The two zoologists painstakingly live-trapped the rats, marked them, released them, and watched which house they went into. Sometimes, by good luck, a trapped female would give birth, and Linsdale and Tevis could see how she behaved towards her young ones and what they did. They put little numbered labels in front of each house to identify it. For the rest they could only watch and listen and take note of every tiny detail. There is probably no other rodent in the world that has been observed for so long and so continuously in one study.

class	**Mammalia**
order	**Rodentia**
family	**Cricetidae**
genus & species	*Neotame cinerea* bushy-tailed wood rat *N. floridana* eastern or Florida pack rat *N. fuscipes* dusky-footed wood rat others

Paddlefish

The paddlefish, a large freshwater bony fish, is related to the sturgeons. It has a long body, and looks like a shark. The skin of the paddlefish is naked except for a few scattered vestigial scales and patches of scales on the tail fin. It has a fairly large head drawn out at the front into a flattened snout shaped like the blade of a canoe paddle. The snout is between one-third and one-half the total length of the fish. At the base of the snout are the small eyes and beneath them a very wide mouth. The gill covers are large and triangular with the apex to the rear, and are drawn out into a point. The pectoral and pelvic fins are medium-sized, as are the single dorsal fin which is set well back on the body and the anal fin which is opposite it. The tail fin is only slightly forked.

There are only 2 species: one, also known as the spoonbill sturgeon, lives in the Mississippi Valley of North America, the other in the Yangtse river system in China. The first is up to 6 ft or more long and weighs 170 lb. The Chinese species, sometimes called the swordbill sturgeon, is reported to reach 23 ft long.

chambers. This sudden opening of the mouth and gill cavities probably produces a suction which draws in small plankton. As the fish swims forward, the plankton is strained from the water by the long gill rakers on the inner sides of the gills. They sometimes eat other fish; shad, for example, have been found in their stomachs.

Vanishing mystery

Although paddlefish are living in a region where there are many people fishing and where there are many naturalists capable of keeping a watch on it, its breeding and spawning behaviour were unknown until a few years ago. Then CA Purkett, in 1960, noticed paddlefishes assembling over a gravel bar in the Osage River when the water level had risen several feet during a spate. He could see them swimming just over the gravel bottom and every now and then one would come to the surface, waggle its tail, and then go down to the bottom again. He assumed correctly that they were spawning and he was later able to work out the story, so ending a long-standing mystery.

The eggs are $\frac{1}{8}$ in. diameter. As they are laid they sink down to the pebbles and stick to them. The larvae hatch within 7 days at ordinary summer temperatures and they are then $\frac{1}{3}$ in. long, with a large head, no eyes, no paddle and no barbels, and each feeds on its large yolk sac. The larvae are encumbered with this yolk sac until it has

appears it grows rapidly. The paddle of one individual that Purkett had under observation grew to 2 in. long in 29 days and had a paddle $\frac{1}{3}$ in. long. Paddlefish kept in ponds grew 6—12 in. in a year, some growing as much as 2 ft in a year, but they are 7—8 years old before they begin to breed.

Relicts of the past

In the early days of the settlement of North America, the paddlefish was not regarded as a fish worth eating. Even today it ranks as only second rate, although the greenish-black eggs are used as caviare. The chief interest in the fish is in its relationship with other fishes. It is classified in the class Pisces, which are also known as bony fishes, yet its skeleton, like that of sharks, is made of cartilage. It also has a short straight intestine with a spiral valve, like sharks. There are other small details of the anatomy which link the paddlefishes with the sharks although in most other respects they are more like bony fishes. They are, in fact, 'missing links', connecting these two main groups. They and the sturgeons are the only surviving members of an order dating back about 100 million years, which was an offshoot from the common ancestors of sharks and bony fishes. The fact that there are only 2 species, one in one part of the world and the other in a widely separated part, suggests that they are a dying race.

American paddlefish looks menacing but is really quite harmless, feeding on small planktonic organisms which it probably detects with its long snout.

Paddling for food

Some people say the paddlefish uses its paddle to probe in the mud for food, while others say it uses the paddle to stir up the mud, but as others have suggested, this seems unlikely for such a sensitive and easily damaged organ. They maintain, and this seems more likely, that as the paddle-fish swims slowly along, it swings its highly sensitive paddle from side to side to detect its food. When it opens its large mouth, the back of the head seems almost to fall away from the rest of the body as the gill covers sag, revealing the capacious gill

been used up. They can be seen swimming erratically up to the surface and down again and when the flood waters begin to subside they are carried downstream or are washed among the rocks. Now we see why the spawning had escaped attention. It takes place on a flood, and when the flood waters recede, there is nothing left to show what has taken place.

The larvae begin to grow their eyes and their barbels within a few hours of being hatched but the paddle does not begin to grow for 2—3 weeks. At first it is only a small bump on the snout but once it

If so, their end is being hastened, at least in North America, where the building of dams and river pollution have even further restricted their range.

class	**Pisces**	
order	**Acipenseriformes**	
family	**Polyodontidae**	
genera	***Polyodon spathula*** American	
& species	***Psephurus gladius*** Chinese	

Pademelon

The name pademelon refers to a particular type of small wallaby. It is said to come from the Aboriginal name paddymalla for small relatives of the kangaroos living in scrub, and another name for them is scrub wallaby.

Pademelons, of which there are four species, are up to 2½ ft in head and body length with the tail up to 1½ ft. The hind foot is not more than 6 in. long. The thick, rounded tail is less tapering than in other wallabies, and is only sparsely coated with hair. The body fur is soft and thick. The feature which distinguishes pademelons from other wallabies is the incisor teeth, the third upper incisor being broad with a notch at the rear edge.

The red-necked pademelon, of the coastal strip of southern Queensland and New South Wales, is grizzled grey, reddish on the neck and shoulders and has a light stripe on the hip. The red-legged pademelon, of Queensland, New South Wales and New Guinea, is mainly russet with more reddish hindlegs and a yellowish hip stripe. The red-bellied pademelon,

of South Australia and Tasmania is greyish-brown with a rufous or orange front and a yellow hip stripe. Bruyn's pademelon of New Guinea, is grey-brown to chocolate-brown with a dark cheek stripe and a white patch above this, and a yellowish hip stripe.

Bolt holes in scrub

Pademelons make tunnel-like runways in the long grass, ferns and bushes. They live in thick scrub and dense forest undergrowth especially in rain forest and forest dominated by eucalyptus, and in swamp areas. The red-bellied pademelon in Tasmania lives in the gullies and scrub where it makes well-trod paths. They sleep hidden in the undergrowth during the day, coming out at dusk to feed, mainly on grass but also to some extent on young shoots.

It has several times been suggested during the past century that wallabies and kangaroos have the habit of chewing the cud. This has been investigated within the last 10 years by BC Mollison of the Commonwealth Scientific and Industrial Research Organisation in Australia. He found that the pademelon sometimes brings up food while resting, perhaps one to two hours after it has finished feeding. The regurgitation is preceded by vigorous heaving move-

ments of the chest and abdomen and the food brought up is retained in the mouth and chewed thoroughly before it is swallowed again. Some of it is spilt from the sides of the mouth onto the ground and it is traces of this kind which show that the rumination is a fairly constant habit. Mollison fed one of the wallabies with bread and biscuit, carrot and apple, but none of these were regurgitated although grass and other herbage that had been eaten previously was brought up to be chewed. So it seems as if this is not a real chewing the cud as with cattle but an ability of wallabies to give a second more thorough chewing to fibrous foods such as grass.

Pademelons cannot win

At the time of the settlement of Australia by Europeans, very large numbers of pademelons could be seen. The Aborigines killed them for food, but had little effect on their numbers. The early white settlers soon realized that their flesh was tender and well-flavoured; like hare according to some reports. Gould, the naturalist working at that time in Australia, compared them with the rabbit in his native England. He even recommended that they should be introduced into England, on large estates and in privately owned forests, for their novelty as well as their flesh. In a short while, however, these small wallabies were being hunted not only for the pot but for their skins which were used for rugs and for trimmings. Thousands were snared for their pelts and at times the destruction was wanton. As if this were not enough, the pademelons were also menaced by bush fires and their habitat was increasingly reduced by land clearance and fencing. This let in the larger wallabies and the kangaroos, who outgrazed them.

Pademelons are slow breeders, with one young, rarely two, at a birth, although the female has four teats in her pouch. Introduced foxes preyed on them, so did the domestic cats and dogs that went wild. Finally, the spread of the introduced rabbit meant that the pademelons had a serious competitor for both food and living space. So although pademelons are said to be still common over parts of their former range they have been seriously reduced in numbers, especially in more settled parts.

Australia in times past

It is of interest to note that the high numbers of pademelons at the time the first Europeans arrived did not mean they were free of enemies. They maintained their numbers in spite of them. De Vis, as long ago as 1883, studied hundreds of bones from the Pliocene period—up to 10 million years ago—and showed that 5% of them were 'pitted, scored, cracked, chopped and crushed'. Within historic times the Tasmanian wolf and the Tasmanian devil were common on the mainland of Australia. There were large numbers of dasyures (p 617) and the wedgetailed eagle, now rare except in remote areas, was one of the commonest birds in the early days of European settlement. All these, and doubtless others, fed on the herbivorous marsupials, and especially on the smaller ones such as the pademelons.

▽ A northern red-legged pademelon, hidden in the undergrowth, hesitates at the end of one of its tunnel-like runways in the long grass and cranes its neck for a better view.

Graham Pizzey: Photo Res

Thumping rivals

There is an irony in the rabbit being added to the list of dangers to the pademelon because the two occupy the same ecological niche. Had those responsible for taking the rabbit to Australia been aware of the similarity between the two animals, they might possibly have been less ready to introduce it. In its grazing and in its habits generally, as well as in its appearance, except for its longer tail and larger size, the pademelon or scrub wallaby is very similar to the scourge of Australia which so readily lives in the scrub conditions and the bush eating all the grass which could feed sheep.

Then comes perhaps the bigger surprise, that the rabbit and the pademelon, which are completely unrelated animals, have one striking trick of behaviour in common. They both thump on the ground with their strong hindfeet as a signal to their fellows that there is danger around.

class	Mammalia
order	Marsupialia
family	Macropodidae
genus & species	*Thylogale billardieri* red-bellied pademelon *T. bruijni* Bruijn's pademelon *T. stigmatica* red-legged pademelon *T. thetis* red-necked pademelon

▽ *The rabbit's competitor: red-bellied pademelon. The rabbit and pademelon are very similar in both habits and appearance and compete especially for grazing. The pademelon appear to be the losers, however, because their numbers continued to dwindle as the rabbit population spread. Previously other predators, now rare, took their toll, and thousands were trapped for their fur.*

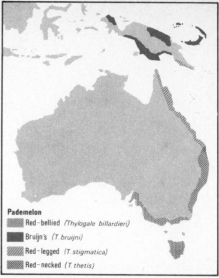

Pademelon

▦ Red-bellied (*Thylogale billardieri*)

■ Bruijn's (*T. bruijni*)

▨ Red-legged (*T. stigmatica*)

▩ Red-necked (*T. thetis*)

Painted snipe

The painted snipe bear only a superficial resemblance to true snipe. Their bills are hard, rigid and shorter than those of true snipe and their flight is slow compared with the swift flight of true snipe. They are closely related to the plovers and sandpipers. The females take the active part in courtship and are brightly coloured whereas the males are more drab.

There are two species of painted snipe. The Old World painted snipe, which is 20 in. long, has a slightly curved bill and its eyes are placed for stereoscopic vision. The ornately patterned females are green above, chestnut on the sides of the head and neck and white underneath. The males are brown barred with black above, and white underneath. Both species have white spectacle-like rings around the eyes and yellowish spots on the wings and tail. The legs are green. The Old World painted snipe lives in many parts of Africa, excluding the densest forests and the deserts, but including Madagascar, in Asia Minor, in Asia south of the Himalayas, in Japan, the Philippines and Australia.

The American painted snipe is about 10 in. long. The bill is more curved at the tip than that of the Old World species and the toes are slightly webbed. The plumage of the sexes is similar but that of the female is brighter. It is almost black above with buff stripes and two oval white spots on the back; the underparts being white. The American painted snipe is not found north of Argentina.

Sleepy heads

Painted snipe are found in flocks of 20–40 or living solitary lives in swamps and marshes or in grassland. They are nocturnal and when disturbed they crouch motionless, only taking flight at the very last moment, just before they are trodden on. In Argentina they are called *dormilōn* or sleepy heads. Their flight is weak and when flushed they merely flutter a short distance with their legs dangling before landing.

Although not usually noisy, the female painted snipe can utter a deep resonant boom, like the noise made by blowing across the mouth of a bottle. This noise is produced in a greatly elongated trachea which lies in four loops. The male on the other hand has a straight trachea and can only give a feeble chirp.

Painted snipe feed on worms, snails, insects, seeds and other plant material such as rice paddy. In Japan some painted snipe have made their diet 90% seeds.

Matriarchal society

As with other birds, such as phalaropes, in which the female has a brighter plumage than the male, it is the female that holds the territory and takes the initiative in

▷ *Family responsibility,* the male **Rostratula benghalensis** *has the task of rearing the young.*

courtship, leaving the male to bring up the family. The Old World painted snipe is polyandrous. Each female may have several mates with nests 5–10 yd apart but she may lay in nests up to 200 yd apart, starting each new clutch at intervals of 12 days. The females of American painted snipe take part in incubation.

Nesting takes place during the rainy season but in some places breeding may take place all the year round, and sometimes twice a year. The nest is built on wet ground. The Old World painted snipe makes an untidy mass of grasses and roots that keep the eggs above water and sometimes the reeds and long grasses that surround the nest are woven together to make a canopy. The American painted snipe lays its eggs on damp ground among herbage, often without a lining.

The Old World painted snipe lays 4 eggs, sometimes 5 or 6. They are cream or yellowish with black blotches and speckling. The American species lays only 2 eggs. They are white with black specks, but sometimes there is so much black they appear to be black with white flecks. Incubation lasts about 3 weeks. If disturbed, the sitting bird does not leave the nest until the intruder is very near. Then it runs silently away or performs a broken wing distraction display. The chicks leave the nest shortly after hatching.

Dual display

For both courting and threatening intruders, painted snipe use a spectacular display. The wings are spread and brought forward either side of the bill and the tail is raised vertically and fanned, with the bird hissing all the time. This display shows the bright spots and markings on the wings and tail to very good effect.

Mr AF D'Ombrain of New South Wales has described the behaviour of a captive painted snipe very graphically: it stops a few feet from the intruder, spreads its wings and tail with a rustle of feathers and poises, swaying backwards and forwards. Then it charges and jabs with its bill. There is no weight behind the jab but the display is impressive enough to persuade anyone of the painted snipe's courage and perhaps to hoodwink them into not searching for its brood.

class	**Aves**
order	**Charadriiformes**
family	**Rostratulidae**
genera & species	*Nycticryphes semicollaris* American *Rostratula benghalensis* Old World

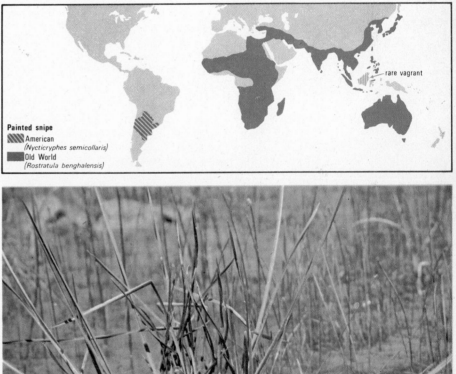

Painted snipe
▨ American
(Nycticryphes semicollaris)
■ Old World
(Rostratula benghalensis)

rare vagrant

Painted turtle

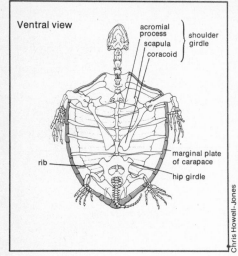

Ventral view

acromial process
scapula } shoulder girdle
coracoid

rib

marginal plate of carapace

hip girdle

Diagrams of a turtle skeleton showing the bony plates forming a box into which the head and limbs can be withdrawn. To support the box the limb girdles are modified and lie inside the encircling ribs. The shoulder girdle has three prongs, a scapula that meets the carapace dorsally, and a long acromial process and a backwardly directed coracoid. These two are fixed with ligaments to the plastron which is removed in the drawing above.

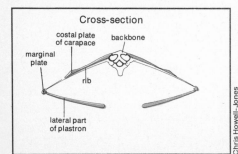

Cross-section

costal plate of carapace   backbone

marginal plate

rib

lateral part of plastron

The painted turtle, also known as the pond turtle or painted terrapin, is the most widely distributed, and in many places the commonest, small turtle in North America. Its smooth, flat carapace is 4–6 in. long. The markings are particularly handsome and the name of painted turtle is well deserved. The carapace is olive-green to black with yellow transverse bands and bright red markings around the edge. The red markings are less conspicuous in older turtles. The legs are marked with red lines and the head and neck with horizontal yellow lines. The plastron is bright yellow and looks as if it has been freshly scrubbed. The single species of painted turtle has four subspecies living in different regions of the United States and southern Canada. **Chrysemys picta picta** is found on the Atlantic coastal plain and **C. picta dorsalis** in the Mississippi valley. These two have a plain yellow plastron. **C. picta marginata** lives in the strip of country between the Allegheny mountains and the Great Lakes. Its plastron has black markings confined to the centre. The most widely distributed subspecies is **C. picta belli** which has black markings around the edges of all the plates of the plastron. It is found in the plains of northern United States and southern Canada and along the east of the Rockies to New Mexico.

Closely related to the painted turtle are the small turtles of the genus **Pseudemys**, known as cooters and sliders. The habits of the two genera are similar.

△ *Dazzled by the photographer's light, a male* **Chrysemys picta** *shuts his eyes and holds on tight with his long claws.*

▷ *Though spending most of their time in the water, painted turtles such as this* **Chrysemys picta marginata** *make the most of summer by basking on logs in the sun.*

A slow life

When food is plentiful painted turtles do not move far, each having a home range of about 100 yd. When they are taken away from their home water, they can find their way back from distances of only about 100 yd, probably by landmarks. Such poor navigation is only to be expected in an animal that does not travel much. When painted turtles set off in search of food they move apparently at random, although they may be able to tell where water is from the brightness of the light which is reflected from the water.

Painted turtles live in ponds, shallow parts of lakes and other quiet stretches of water. They may be found in the sluggish, well vegetated parts of streams. Their distribution is determined by the abundance of water plants, their chief food. They are particularly fond of long, trailing plants that float on the surface. Aquatic insects, including beetles and dragonfly larvae, snails, tadpoles and fishes are also eaten. If food runs low, as in a drought, painted turtles migrate to other stretches of water.

Apart from journeys in search of fresh food supplies, painted turtles rarely come on land. Like all turtles, however, they lay their eggs on land, and they also climb onto banks or logs to bask, during the morning and afternoon but they avoid the midday sun. It has been suggested that one benefit of basking is that it dries the skin of parasitic leeches, causing them to drop off.

Fast swimming suitors

In the spring and early summer the male painted turtle, which is distinguished by his longer tail and claws on his forefeet, seeks out and courts the female. He swims after her, overtakes, and turns to face her head on. The female continues swimming and the male has to swim backwards, but as he goes he brushes the long claws of his forefeet against the female's cheeks. If a female is receptive she sinks to the bottom of the pond and allows the male to mate with her.

Eggs are laid in May—July. The females crawl onto land and dig their nests up to 100 yd or more from the water's edge. They dig the nest with the hindfeet and sometimes soften the soil with urine. Each egg is carefully positioned in the nest by the hindfeet. The clutch averages 7—10 eggs and after it is completed the female turtle fills in the hole and stamps the soil down.

The eggs hatch in the autumn, except in the most northerly part of the range where they may not hatch until the following spring. The newly-hatched turtles are about 1 in. long. They try to make their way to the water almost immediately, before they can be caught by their numerous enemies. They are mature at 4 years, when they are $3\frac{1}{2}$ in. long.

Seeking warmth

In the northern parts of their range, painted turtles hibernate, burrowing into mud or sheltering in a muskrat hole from November to March. When they emerge in the spring their pond may still be covered with ice and it has been found that they will sometimes move some distance from their 'home' pond at these times, and travel up the streams that flow in or out. To find what, if anything, guided the turtles, they were placed in Y-shaped tubes. The turtles could choose which arm of the Y to swim up and it was found that they responded to the temperature of the water in the arms. Turtles do not become active until 10°C/50°F. If the water in which they had been living was too cool they swam up the warmer arm, but if used to warm water they followed the cool current. In the spring, then, the turtles sometimes leave their ponds if they are still too cold, and swim up the slightly warmer streams; as their bodies warm up, the turtles become more active and start feeding.

class	**Reptilia**
order	**Chelonia**
family	**Emydidae**
genus & species	*Chrysemys picta*

Showing off. **Pseudemys scripta**, *a close relative of the painted turtles, turns on its side to reveal the beautiful markings on its plastron.*

Palm chat

The palm chat is a drab bird which would pass almost unnoticed in its woodland home if it was not for the large 'apartment houses' that it builds. It is about 7 in. long, olive-grey above and its white underparts are streaked with brown. The rump is dark green, the tail fairly long and the wings short and rounded. The sexes are similar and juveniles differ from adults in having dark brown necks and light brown rumps.

The palm chat is the sole representative of the family Dulidae and lives only on the West Indian island of Hispaniola, which is divided into the Dominican Republic and Haiti, and on nearby Gonave Island where it has a more local distribution.

Chattering groups

The palm chat is one of the most prominent birds in Hispaniola. It is common over most of the island where the royal palm grows in abundance, and is therefore absent only from areas of dense rain forest and the mountain peaks. Small groups of up to 20 palm chats can be seen flying together in search of food and they roost together at night. Each group is made up of several pairs and their young. The groups chatter harshly as they fly about. The centre of the group's activities is the large nest of sticks that is built at the top of a royal palm or, more rarely, a pine tree.

Fruit and flowers

Palm chats eat fruit and flowers but they do not appear to be a pest. They have been found eating palm berries and have been seen plucking flowers of *Cordia* in flight, but landing to eat them.

Apartment houses

In the spring, from March to June, the palm chats build their nests or repair old ones. The first remarkable feature of the nests is the size of the twigs used in their construction. The nests are woven from twigs ranging from 1–3 ft long and up to 1 in. in cross-section. It is no mean feat for a palm chat, no bigger than a skylark, to carry such twigs from the ground to the nest as much as 50 ft high in a palm tree. The twigs are carried in the bill and the palm chat may have to pause and rest on its way up to the nest. The twigs are loosely woven at first and then tightened to form an untidy mass about 3 ft across. The nest is securely anchored to the palm fronds but when the fronds eventually die the nest falls to the ground.

About four pairs of palm chats live in one nest, but there are never more than one or two pairs in the nests built in pine trees,

▽ *The palm chat's name is derived from its distribution which is identical with that of the royal palm tree on the island of Hispaniola.*

which presumably provide less suitable foundations. The pairs work together in building the nest, all pulling and tugging at the twigs to force them into place. Breeding is, however, not communal for the nest is divided into separate compartments in which each pair raises its family. The nest is made up of units each consisting of a chamber, 4–5 in. across, with tightly woven walls and a tunnel leading to the exterior. There are also small, ill-defined tunnels leading inside the nest so the palm chats can move about under cover.

The nesting chambers are lined with shredded bark and grass. Very little is known about the palm chat's breeding habits except that they lay 4 eggs and the young stay with their parents for some time after they have left the nest. The nests are also used as roosts outside the breeding season.

Harmless parasite

We know little about the diseases and parasites of animals unless they are of domestic animals or are likely to be transferred to humans. Animals undoubtedly suffer from diseases but we do not often see obviously diseased or parasitised animals because they are usually killed by predators as soon as the malady takes effect. It has, however, been known for some time that palm chats are parasitised by a fly, *Philornis pici*. The eggs are laid in nestling birds and the larvae develop in a sac under the skin of the head or wing. Eventually the larvae burrow out and drop to the ground where they make a cocoon of earth particles glued together. Sometimes as many as 90% of the birds examined bear these flies but they do not seem to be harmed in any way. This is true of all real parasites; those that harm their hosts, like the ichneumon (p 1161), should be called parasitoids.

class	**Aves**
order	**Passeriformes**
family	**Dulidae**
genus & species	***Dulus dominicus***

Peter J Green

Peter J Green

▷△ *A house with a view. The palm chats build their nest as high as 50 ft up a tree. Several pairs of palm chats use the same nest, each pair occupying a separate compartment inside and all combining to build this large home.*

▷ *This untidy bundle of twigs is a section of a palm chat's nest removed from a tree. It is constructed with very large twigs, which are sometimes almost too big for the birds which often have to pause on their way up to the nest.*

Palm civet

There are six species of palm civet in southern Asia and one in Africa. They are long-bodied and short-legged, with sharp muzzles, and with the tail as long or slightly longer than head and body. The best known are the musangs or toddy cats. One species **Paradoxurus hermaphroditus** ranges from Ceylon and India through southern China and southeast Asia to the Philippines. Two others are from southern India and Ceylon. Just over 4 ft in total length, they are grey to brown with dark back stripes and spots on the flanks, and with white patches on the head. The small-toothed palm civet, which ranges from Assam to Borneo, is much the same length but with a longer tail, and is greyish to bright orange tawny with dark stripes along the back and a white stripe on the muzzle. It gets the name from its very small back teeth. The similar but more slender Celebes palm civet is rare and confined to that island. It is 5 ft long, has more grey on the face, throat and belly and has a ringed tail. The masked palm civet is 4½ ft total length, lives in Kashmir and southern China eastwards to Hainan and Formosa, is also found on the Andaman Islands and has been introduced to Japan. The African palm civet or two-spotted civet, 4 ft overall, ranges from Senegal to the Sudan and southwards to Rhodesia and Angola. It is grey to brown tinged with buff or chestnut, with lighter underparts and it has two white spots on the shoulders which give it one of its names.

Silent night hunters—of fruit

Although very similar in appearance and habits, the palm civets differ from the true civets in several anatomical details, including the kind of teeth they have. They live mainly in trees but also sometimes come to the ground to feed. They are nocturnal, the pupil of the eye being vertical as in many other nocturnal animals. They are agile in leaping from branch to branch. In climbing they are helped by their sharp curved claws and, in most species, by the naked soles. The pink skin of the soles is carried back from the toe pads to the heel.

Most palm civets are fairly silent animals so little is known about their calls. Some use a kind of mewing, with light snarls when alarmed. During the day palm civets rest in holes in trees, among vines or other dense foliage. The toddy cat often lives in or near houses, in the gardens, in dry drains or in thatch, or even in suburbs of large towns.

Wine-bibbers

The differences in the teeth, as compared with true civets, show the palm civets to be less carnivorous. Generally, the teeth are weaker and the carnassials, the pair of teeth on each side of the mouth, used for slicing flesh, are less well developed in the palm civets than in more typical carnivores. All six species eat mainly plant food, especially fruits, but also seeds, and even roots in the case of the masked palm civet. To this they add animal food such as small birds and mammals, insects and their grubs, and sometimes earthworms. The masked palm civet also catches fish and it has the reputation of being a good ratter; and unlike so many ratters it does not seem to interfere with poultry. The African palm civet goes for even bigger prey, such as pottos. The Indian palm civet is called the toddy cat from its addiction to fermenting sap. The local peoples tap the palm trees, hanging cups on the trunks to catch the sap for wine-making. Before this is collected the palm civet often takes a share.

Breeding

There are 2–4 young in a litter, born in a hollow tree or among rocks. There are usually 2 litters a year, and gestation lasts about 2 months. The young grow to full size in about 3 months. Palm civets, and especially the Indian species, are often kept in zoos where they have lived to over 15 years of age.

Skunk-like tactics

Small and medium-sized carnivores usually have few enemies. Some of the palm civets, besides their sharp teeth, use their anal glands as a means of defence. The toddy cats especially, and to a lesser extent the masked palm civet, give out a highly obnoxious odour from these glands, which is more in keeping with the skunks. It has been suggested that the white markings on the faces of the toddy cats and the masked palm civet act as warning signals to predators to keep away. It is noticeable that the two palm civets so far not reported as using the skunk-defence do not have the white face markings, although one of them, the African palm civet, has white spots on the shoulders.

Famous scholar deceived

The famous French scientist, Baron Cuvier, gave the Indian palm civet the scientific name *Paradoxurus* in 1821. This was soon anglicized to paradoxure in England, but this dropped out of use by the end of the 19th century. *Urus* means tail, and the animal with the paradoxical tail was a palm civet in the Paris zoo that had its tail coiled in a peculiar way. This permanent coiled position is a condition more common years ago, when zoo animals were less well looked after, as it is the result of a disease due to the effects of captivity.

class	**Mammalia**
order	**Carnivora**
family	**Viverridae**
genera & species	*Arctogalidia trivirgata* small-toothed **Nandinia binotata** *African* **Paguma larvata** *masked* **Paradoxurus hermaphroditus** *Indian or musang* *others*

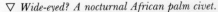

▽ *Banded palm civets* **Hemigalus derbyanus**. *Their strong, retractile claws aid them in climbing.*

▽ *Wide-eyed? A nocturnal African palm civet.*

roebild

Jane Burton: Photo Res

Palm dove

The palm dove is a relative of the collared dove, p 485. It is well-known in many parts of Africa and Asia, and has many alternative names. Usually it is the laughing dove but other names include Senegal dove, town dove, village or garden dove and little brown dove. The palm dove is half the size of the domestic pigeon, with comparatively short wings and a long tail. The head, neck and breast are a dark mauvish pink merging into the white of the belly. The back is reddish brown, the rump slate blue and the tail brown, edged with grey and white. The wings are largely slate blue. Around the neck there is a bib of colourful feathers, each forked and black at the base with golden tips. The female is paler than the male.

The palm dove is found in many parts of Africa, except the Sahara and Madagascar. In Asia it ranges from Turkey and Arabia to eastern India. Palm doves also live on Malta and have been introduced to parts of Australia. Those found in Turkey and Asia Minor were probably introduced by man, like those in Australia.

Living with man

Palm doves are birds of open country such as dry scrub and bush where permanent water is near, but they are also found in forest clearings. They have become dependent on man in many places, so earning their common names of town, village and garden dove. They are very tame and feed largely on spilt seeds such as millet, wheat and maize, their natural food being the seeds of a variety of wild plants.

Although they live in pairs, several dozen palm doves can be seen feeding together in streets or on farms, or on the rocks where cassava is pounded. When they are feeding a group of laughing doves argue amongst themselves, hooting and moaning quietly and occasionally adding force to their bickering with pecks. The flight of palm doves is usually slow but they will fly very fast if chased by a hawk. Their main call is 4—6 'coos' which sound like a bubbling laugh, hence the name of laughing dove. This call is attractive, if monotonous, and combined with its tameness and pretty plumage has made the palm dove a popular neighbour in many places.

Light, but strong nests

In the tropics palm doves nest at any time of the year but most of the eggs are laid during the rainy season. Nests are built in the forks of trees or at the bases of palm fronds, and sometimes on ledges of buildings or in thatch. The male collects the material while the female builds. As is usual with pigeons and doves, the nest appears to be very flimsy and hardly able to support the weight of the 2 white eggs and the sitting parent, and at times the eggs show through the bottom of the nest. Malcolm MacDonald, in his book *Birds in My Indian Garden,* is at pains to dispel the idea that the pigeon family throw their nests together carelessly. A palm dove nest in his garden lasted for at least 7 months, even surviving the monsoons. Mr MacDonald took several abandoned palm dove nests apart and found that they were made of 80—140 twigs and rootlets that were woven into a very firm pad. To call the nest flimsy because of its appearance would be the same as condemning a suspension bridge because it is hung on a lattice-work of cables. Like other doves, the male palm dove has a spectacular display flight: it flies up, claps its wings and then glides in a circle with wings and tail spread. The display flight is used to advertise the male's presence to females and other males. When courting the male bows rapidly to her, with his head horizontal which shows off the colourful bib on his neck. At the same time he coos softly. If the male palm dove's bowing is acceptable to the female the pair engages in billing, which leads to mating.

Billing and cooing

The term 'billing and cooing' is a popular term for human courtship but it is derived from dove courtship. To be correct we should speak of 'cooing and billing' because the cooing and bowing precedes billing. In some kinds of doves billing is no more than a touching of the bills but the gesture is derived from courtship feeding. The male offers his open bill, the female inserts hers and food is transferred. In the palm dove no food is passed but the male still makes movements as if he is regurgitating food.

The courtship of doves and pigeons is a pretty sight and billing gives it a human touch. Malcolm MacDonald certainly found this so as he describes the difference in the calls of the collared dove and palm dove by saying that the three 'coos' of the collared dove sound like 'I lo-ove you' whereas the palm dove has two extra notes and intones 'Darling, I lo-ove you'.

class	**Aves**
order	**Columbiformes**
family	**Columbidae**
genus & species	***Streptopelia senegalensis***

The next-door neighbour? This pretty bird with its bubbling laugh is often quite tame which has earned it the names of town, village and garden dove.

AS Cheke

Palm squirrel

There are three kinds of squirrels with this name, and sometimes the giant squirrels **Ratufa** of India and Malaya are included among them. The best known are the palm squirrels of southern Asia, including Ceylon, India, Pakistan and the Andaman Islands. The five species of Asian palm squirrels are often called striped palm squirrels because they are striped much like chipmunks (p 436). They have a dense soft fur that is light greyish brown to almost black most of the year, but shows reddish on the head from December to May. There are three light stripes on the back, occasionally there is a further short stripe on each flank. Asian palm squirrels are about 7 in. long head and body with about the same length of bushy tail.

The two species of African palm squirrels are up to 2 ft long, of which about half is a bushy tail. One species lives in the Gabon, Cameroons and Congo. The coat colour is a mixture of red and black, and is yellowish on the underparts, where the hair is often scanty and the skin at times almost naked. The second species, in Ghana and Sierra Leone, is reddish with buff patches and some yellow on the underparts. Again the hair on the underparts is sparse, the skin often naked.

The third kind are sometimes spoken of as the oil-palm or African giant squirrels. There are two species, one in West Africa, Liberia to Ghana, the other farther south, from Kenya to Angola. The first has grizzled fur and a slender black tail, the second is tawny olive to nearly black shading to white or buff underparts and cheeks white to greyish. Its bushy tail is sometimes banded black and white. The length of head and body is 13 in., the tail 16 in.

George S Candsdale

△ *Rare picture of an equally rare animal, an African palm squirrel* **Epixerus ebii**.

▽ *The stripes on an Indian palm squirrel* **F. palmarum** *are good camouflage in the wild.*

Popperfoto

The Indian giant squirrel **Ratufa indica**.

Peter Jackson: Photo Res

The oil-palm squirrel or 'booming' squirrel as it is sometimes called enjoys a good meal.

George S Candsdale

All squirrels under the skin

The different species of striped palm squirrels live in very varied places from open palm forest and scrub at low altitudes to dense jungle with tall trees. Their habits are like those of tree squirrels of the northern hemisphere and like them some palm squirrels live near human settlements even to nesting in roof spaces. African palm squirrels usually live in cavities in trees.

One species *Protoxerus stangeri* is also known as the booming squirrel from the booming sounds it makes when alarmed. Otherwise its voice is a bird-like twittering.

All grist to the mill

Striped palm squirrels feed by day, in the trees or on the ground, on seeds, nuts, stems, bark, buds, leaves and flowers, as well as insects and their grubs. They sometimes take cocoa pods and the buds and seeds of silk cotton trees from which kapok is obtained. They also enjoy eating nectar from the silky oak—which is not a true oak —and in doing so become dusted with pollen and so may act as pollinators. African palm squirrels feed in trees and on the ground, especially on nuts of the oil palm. They have also been known to gnaw fresh ivory and bones.

Surplus males

In the Indian palm squirrel there are as many females born as males but by the time

maturity is reached the males outnumber the females. At breeding time a female is chased by several males who fight among themselves while she waits on a nearby tree making peeping calls at her fighting suitors. The successful male then mates with her. Although mating is prolonged, up to 20 minutes, the male stays with the female for only a day. The female builds a nest on the branches of a tree or in a hollow. It is globular, made of dry grass or other fibrous materials such as bits of cloth, jute sacking, animal hair and feathers. One was seen to card a mass of cottonwool, using her incisors and forepaws. Another, in captivity, pulled out the hairs from her own tail to bind the dry grass of the nest. The main breeding season is March—September, but there may be 3 litters a year with 2—4, usually 3, in a litter. The young are born naked, with pink skin, and measure 4 in. long of which more than half is tail. Their eyes are unopened, their ears folded and they cannot crawl until a few days old, and then only feebly. The ears open at 7 days, the eyes between 15 —25 days. Weaning is at 25—30 days and the young have grown a full coat of hair, shorter than in the adult but with the same colour and pattern by 5—8 weeks. They are then half the size of the parent. The young females are sexually mature at 6—8 months of age, but there is no information on the age at which young males become sexually mature and search for females.

Squirrel plays 'possum

The North American opossum (p 1615) is well known for its habit of 'shamming dead', and there are only a few reports of other mammals having done this. One is the Indian palm squirrel. DR Sharma, S Sivaram and K Verma have described what happened when one of them shot at a palm squirrel with an airgun. The squirrel fell onto a lower branch as if it had been hit. It hung upside down from the branch, clinging by its hindfeet, the head hanging limply, the eyes half-closed, and the grip of the hindfeet showing signs of relaxing. All were convinced the squirrel had been fatally injured although no blood was showing. Then one of them climbed up the tree and stretched out a hand to take the squirrel. But it suddenly started moving and quickly ran down the tree, running away faster than any of them could follow.

class	**Mammalia**
order	**Rodentia**
family	**Sciuridae**
genera & species	***Epixerus spp*** *African palm squirrels* ***Funambulus spp*** *Indian palm squirrels* ***Protoxerus stangeri*** *oil-palm squirrel, others*

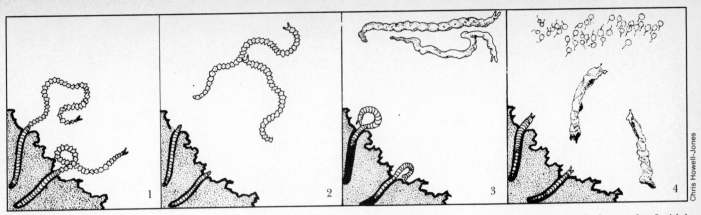

Palolo worm

Twice a year, and with incredible regularity, half of this worm develops almost into another animal, and swarms of these invade the sea to breed. Palolo worms measure about 16 in. long, and, like their relatives the ragworms, are divided into a large number of segments each with a pair of paddle-like appendages that bear gills. The head has several sensory tentacles and an evertable pharynx which has stout teeth. Males are reddish-brown and females bluish-green.

The palolo worm lives in coral reefs off Samoa and Fiji in the southern Pacific, but related worms live in shallow seas in other tropical regions.

Mass wedding

Palolo worms riddle coral with the tubes that they dig in the reefs, in crevices, or under rocks. They are very difficult to extract whole because their long, fragile bodies are firmly anchored in the tubes.

Towards the breeding season the back half of the body of a palolo worm alters drastically. The muscles and other internal organs degenerate while the reproductive organs in each segment grow rapidly. The limbs become more paddle-like. In due course the palolo worm backs up its tunnel, with the head innermost, until the modified portion of its body is protruding. This part breaks free and swims to the surface as a separate animal, complete with rudimentary eyes with which to navigate. The remaining front half stays in the tube and regenerates the lost portion.

These free-swimming portions of the palolo worm were once thought to be the complete animal but they are little more than bags of eggs and sperms. On reaching the surface these are discharged and the empty skins sink to the bottom to be devoured by fish. The eggs are fertilised as they float at the surface and from them free-swimming larvae develop.

This behaviour is a kind of reproduction by proxy, with the worm staying in the safety of its tube while releasing a part of itself to go out and mate. This is incredible enough but the spectacular feature is that all the reproductive parts are released at the same time each year. When this happens the sea becomes a writhing mass of millions of worms and is milky with eggs and sperms.

△ *Spectacular life cycle of Pacific palolo worm. As the breeding season approaches the adults reverse their positions in burrows; the back half alters drastically as the reproductive organs grow rapidly (1). This part breaks free and swims to the surface (2). The remaining adult portions reverse to a normal position. The eggs and sperm sections develop further with internal segments breaking down to give a single sac (3), which soon bursts releasing eggs and sperm so random fertilisation takes place (4). This is neatly timed—millions of worms mating at once.*

Swarming is limited to the neap tides of October and November. It occurs at dawn, the day before and the day on which the moon is in its last quarter.

The advantages

How the palolo worms calculate the time of spawning so accurately is not known; they certainly cannot watch the phases of the moon from their burrows. Presumably they have a very accurate internal 'clock' which is regulated by a combination of a diurnal

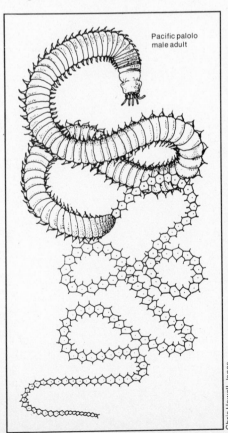

Pacific palolo male adult

rhythm of night and day and of tidal changes. In addition to this, there is probably the same stimulus as is mentioned under oyster (p 1656). In oysters, sea urchins and some other marine animals the first sperms released touch off a wholesale spawning. It is possible that the first palolo worms to shed their rear portions into the water for spawning give out a chemical, possibly a hormone, which touches off a similar wholesale action among all the others in the reef that are ready to spawn.

If the mechanism is obscure, the advantages are obvious. By releasing all eggs and sperms in one or two highly synchronised batches the chances of fertilisation are very much increased. In many marine animals, especially those that are sedentary and release eggs and sperms in the sea, there is often a restricted breeding season which increases the chances of the sex cells meeting. Oysters, for instance, 'spat' more frequently at new and full moons than at other times, but few animals attain the narrow limits achieved by the palolo worm. A very closely related species in the West Indies spawns in the third quarter of the June and July moons, while another worm *Ceratocephale osawai* spawns off Japan at the new and full moons of October and November. The grunion (p 972) also has a narrowly regulated mating season.

Seasonal delicacy

For a long time the spawning palolo worms have been caught in vast numbers by the peoples of the South Pacific. Chiefs living by the sea send them inland as presents for they are highly esteemed raw or cooked. In Fiji the time of swarming is heralded first by the flowering of the scarlet aloals and the seasea. Then they know they must watch for the moon being on the horizon as dawn breaks. Ten days after this the palolo worm spawns, The first swarm is 'Mbalolo lailai'—little palolo, and the second 'Mbalolo levu' —large palolo. On the island of Savaii the swarming is forecast, three days beforehand by the mass migration of land crabs down to the sea to spawn themselves.

phylum	**Annelida**
class	**Polychaeta**
family	**Eunicidae**
genus & species	*Eunice viridis* Pacific *E. fucata* West Indies

Panda

This black and white bear-like carnivore has leapt from obscurity to worldwide fame in less than a century. Also called the giant panda and, by the Chinese, **beishung**, the white bear, it was first made known to the western world in 1869, by the French missionary, Père David. It has usurped the name from the cat-bear (p 391), which was originally called panda, but is now called the lesser or red panda, or cat-bear, to distinguish the two.

The panda is stockily built, with a 6 ft long body and a mere stump of a tail and weighs 300 lb. Its thick, dense fur is white except for the black legs and ears, black round the eyes and on the shoulders. There are 5 clawed toes on each foot and each forefoot has a small pad which acts as a thumb for grasping. The cheek teeth are broad and the skull is deep with prominent ridges for the attachment of strong muscles needed in chewing fibrous shoots. It lives in the cold damp bamboo forests on the hillsides of eastern Tibet and Szechwan in southwest China.

to the Moscow zoo, and Chi-chi, the female in the London zoo. In 1966 Chi-chi was taken to Moscow by air but no mating took place, and An-an was brought to London in 1968 with no more success. It is believed that pandas mate in spring, and that probably one or two cubs are born in the following January, each cub weighing 3 lb at birth. Several cubs have been born in Chinese zoos. On September 9, 1963, a male cub Ming-ming was born to Li-li and Pi-pi in Peking zoo, and a female cub, Ling-ling, was born on September 4, 1964, to the same parents. A third cub Hua-hua, a male, was born to Chiao-chiao on October 10, 1965. According to Mare Ribaud, a French photographer writing in *Natural History*, April 1966, Ming-ming and Ling-ling were produced by artificial insemination. Presumably the same is true for Hua-hua.

▷ *Chinese mother love. Although breeding has not been achieved in the western world, Chinese zoos have bred pandas. The young one seen here cradled in its mother's arms was born at Peking Zoo. Although it was thought that Peking Zoo had a breeding unit of pandas, Mare Ribaud, a French photographer wrote in 1966 that artificial insemination was practised. Breeding behaviour in the wild is still unknown. It is thought that oestrus is in April with a gestation period of 148 days. There are differing views on its numbers in the wild. The director of Peking Zoo in 1966 did not commit himself to any estimate of numbers but thought the number was small. On the other hand he thought the numbers would increase as the local people understood the interest of the animal.*

Zool Soc London

Conservation co-operation. With the rare species quota increasing each year it is important for today's zoos to try to breed these rarities. Often a zoo has only one sex of an endangered animal, so the director will try to arrange a 'marriage' with the opposite sex if another zoo has the needed partner. 'An-an' (above) of Moscow Zoo and 'Chi-chi' of London Zoo were the only live pandas of the western world in the sixties. The Russians allowed Chi-chi to visit An-an in 1966 (right) but this encounter proved a failure. Chi-chi returned home in disgrace after refusing all An-an's advances. In 1968-69 An-an spent 10 months with Chi-chi in London Zoo but even after sex hormone treatment she still refused to be mated.

Habits unknown . . .

Pandas are solitary animals except in the breeding season. They live mainly on the ground but will climb trees when pursued by dogs. They are active all the year. Little more is known of the habits in the wild of this secretive animal which lives in inaccessible country. When live pandas were first taken to zoos it was thought they lived solely on bamboo shoots. Later it was learned that during the 10—12 hours a day they spend feeding they eat other plants, such as grasses, gentians, irises and crocuses, and also some animal food. This last includes small rodents, small birds and fishes flipped out of water with their paws.

Breeding unknown . . .

Little is known about the panda's breeding habits in spite of attempts to induce a mating between An-an, the male panda belonging

Ian Watson

Via dolorosa

In 1869 Père Armand David of the Lazarist Missionary Society, and an experienced naturalist, came upon the skin of an animal in a Chinese farmhouse in Szechwan which he did not recognize. He sent it to Paris and later sent more skins. Not until 1937, however, was the first live panda seen outside China. Theodore and Kermite Roosevelt had shot one in the 1920's and in 1936 two other Americans, Ruth and William Harkness, with the animal collector Tangier Smith, captured several. They quarrelled, presumably over the spoils, and all the pandas died except one, which Ruth Harkness delivered to the Chicago zoo where it was named Su-lin. Another, given the name Mei-mei, reached the same zoo in 1938. In December the same year a young female, Ming, aged 7 months and two young males, Tang and Sung, reached the London zoo. The two males died before the female reached maturity, and she died in December

1944. In May 1946, the government of the Szechwan Province presented a male, Lien-ho, to the London zoo and he lived until 1950. By 1967 there were a score of pandas in various zoos, 16 or more in Chinese zoos, An-an in Moscow and Chi-chi in London.

Whether giant pandas are as rare as is sometimes supposed is a matter for speculation. If it is, this could be due in no small measure to the way they have been treated. Although the species is now protected it was formerly hunted by the local Chinese, and the history of western animal collectors does nothing to offset this. The story of Chi-chi gives point to this. In 1957, Heini Demmer, then living in Nairobi, was commissioned by an American zoo to negotiate the exchange of a collection of East African animals for one panda. He reached Peking zoo with his cargo, was given the choice of one of three pandas, chose Chi-chi, the youngest, and took charge of her on May 5 1958. Chi-chi had been captured by a Chinese team of collectors on July 5 1957,

Bamboo shoots are not the sole food of pandas— other plants and some animal food is eaten.

and was reckoned then to be 6 months old. She had been taken to Peking zoo and cared for night and day by a Chinese girl. By the time Demmer had taken charge of Chi-chi the United States had broken off diplomatic relations with the Chinese People's Republic, so she became automatically a banned import. Demmer took her on a tour of European zoos during the summer of 1958, by car, rail and plane, reaching the London zoo, where she was bought, on September 26.

After such treatment perhaps it is not surprising she refuses to be mated!

class	**Mammalia**
order	**Carnivora**
family	**Procyonidae**
genus & species	*Ailuropoda melanoleuca*

Pangolin

Pangolins have sometimes been called animated pine cones because the hair on their backs has been converted into large overlapping brown scales covering the head, back, tail and legs. The underside of the body is, however, soft and hairy. The pangolin's body is long, with a long tail. Its snout is pointed, with a small mouth at the end and with toothless jaws. Its long tongue can be thrust out for nearly a foot. The pangolin has small eyes and hidden ears. Its legs are short and the five toes on each foot have stout claws used in digging. In Africa there are four species of pangolin, or scaly anteater as it is sometimes called, and three in southern Asia.

The large African pangolin of equatorial Africa is 5 ft or more long as is the giant pangolin. Other African species are the black-bellied or long-tailed pangolin and the small-scaled tree pangolin, from West Africa to Uganda, both 3 ft total length. The largest Asiatic species is the Indian pangolin, 3½ ft long. The Chinese pangolin, of Nepal, southern China, Hainan and Formosa, and the Malayan pangolin are both under 3 ft.

Ground dwellers and tree climbers

Most of these strange scaly beasts climb trees, using their sharp claws and their tail, either wrapping the tail around a branch and sometimes hanging by it, or using it as a support by pressing it against the trunk of a tree. The giant and Indian pangolins both live on the ground, however, the latter sometimes climbing trees for safety when chased. All pangolins are active mainly at night, the ground-living forms resting in burrows dug by other animals, the tree dwellers resting in cavities in the trunks. When on the ground they walk on the sides of their fore-feet, or on their knuckles, with their long claws turned inwards. They will sometimes walk on their hindlegs with their body raised semi-erect, their tail raised above the ground as a counterpoise.

Hot meals

This attitude, with the tail supporting the erect or semi-erect body, is also used when a pangolin is tearing open a termites' nest with its long front claws and exploring the galleries of the nests with its long tongue. The tongue is sticky and is flicked in and out to carry the termites into the mouth. Ants are also eaten: adults, pupae, larvae, and eggs. The tough skin of the head protects the pangolin from attacks by soldier termites or the stings of ants. The nostrils and ear openings can be closed and the eyes are protected by thick lids. Ants crawling onto the body are shaken off, and those swallowed are soon ground by the thick muscular walls of the stomach and by the small pebbles that the pangolin swallows. Tree-climbing pangolins eat mainly tree ants. A pangolin drinks by rapidly darting its tongue out and in.

Pangolins do not usually survive long in

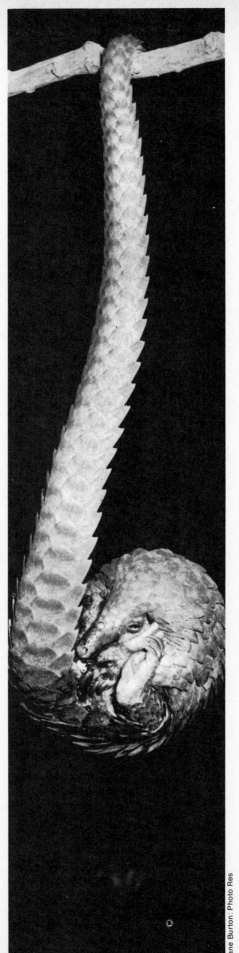

captivity, a few weeks at most, and post mortem examinations have shown their digestive organs to be heavily parasitized. One lived over 4 years in the New York Zoological Park on finely ground raw beef, cooked cereal, evaporated milk, ant's eggs, with occasional raw egg, cod-liver oil and vitamin concentrate. But it seems likely that termites and ants are essential to them.

Babies ride pick-a-back

Very little is known about the breeding habits of pangolins since they fail to breed in captivity. They have one young, rarely two, in the wild, probably every year. The scales do not harden until the second day after birth. Later the baby rides on the mother clinging to her tail.

Ant-bathing

The main enemy of pangolins is probably man. Animals, such as leopards, sometimes examine them but are, it seems, put off by their scales. They are killed locally for their flesh and their scales are used for ornaments and charms, as well as for their supposed medicinal value. In Africa boys are sent into the burrow to put a rope round a pangolin's tail, to drag it out. Its defence is to roll up but even a light touch on a pangolin's body makes it snap its sharp-edged scales flat and this may act as a deterrent. Some pangolins, possibly all, can give off an obnoxious fluid from glands under their tail. They are said sometimes to hiss when molested.

There is a story that pangolins allow ants to crawl under their scales, then snap the scales down to kill them, afterwards eating the dead ants. The probable explanation is that the scales are snapped down because the observer touches the pangolin, or makes a movement that alarms it. That they do take an ant bath seems likely. There are local beliefs that a pangolin will lie in an ants' nest, allowing the insects to crawl over it, and under its scales onto the soft skin beneath. There are reports about a variety of animals taking ant baths. It is presumed they get satisfaction from the formic acid stimulating the skin. Cecil S Webb, an animal collector, was of the opinion that a pangolin's skin absorbed this acid and it was essential to the animal's health. He suggested this was one reason why they failed to survive in captivity.

An animal puzzle

Pangolin skins brought back from Africa and Asia were known to the Romans and also to the scientists of the 16th century and later. All were puzzled by them, as were the peoples in whose countries they lived. Arabs called the pangolin *abu-khirfa*, 'father of cattle', the Indians named it *bajur-kit*, 'jungle fish', the Chinese name was *lungli*, 'dragon carp', and the Romans called it an earth-crocodile. The name 'pangolin' is from the Malay *peng-goling*, the roller, from its habit of rolling into a ball. Pangolin skins puzzled the scholars of Europe until early 19th century when Baron Cuvier decided it was a mammal.

It's easy when you have the equipment! A small scaled pangolin hangs by its prehensile tail.

Jane Burton: Photo Res

1653

Animated pine cones

◁ *A black-bellied pangolin illustrates its common description — 'animated pine cones'.*
▷ *Small-scaled youngster grips to mother's tail while she is curled up asleep.*
▽ *A long elastic tongue protruded from a toothless mouth of a large African pangolin seeks out ants and termites on which it feeds.*

◁ *Ants swarm over the scales of a giant pangolin intent on eating all it can.*
▷ *Pangolins are quite widespread but not very numerous in any part of their range.*
▷▷ *A pangolin rolls itself into a ball.*

class	**Mammalia**
order	**Pholidota**
family	**Manidae**
genus & species	***Manis crassicaudata*** *Indian*
	M. gigantea *large African*
	M. javanica *Malayan*
	M. longicaudata *black-bellied*
	M. pentadactyla *Chinese*
	M. temminckii *giant*
	M. tricuspis *small-scaled tree*

Pangolin
- Giant *(Manis temminckii)*
- Small-scaled tree *(M. tricuspis)*
- Black-bellied *(M. longicaudata)*
- Indian *(M. crassicaudata)*
- Chinese *(M. pentadactyla)*
- Malayan *(M. javanica)*

Paper wasp

Paper wasps are closely related to the common wasps and hornets of the genus **Vespula** *and* **Vespa.** *There is little to choose between them in appearance, but the thorax and abdomen of the paper wasp are pear-shaped where they join, more like an hourglass than the rounded thorax and abdomen of the other wasps. In habits paper wasps differ by making small nests that are not enclosed by a papery sheath, and the cells containing eggs and larvae are open.*

Paper wasps are found all over the world in tropical and temperate regions. They do not live in Britain but are very common in North America.

often get warm, the nests are kept cool by the wasps fanning their wings, and they may bring water to regurgitate over the comb.

The queen paper wasp constructs the nest from paper which she makes by rasping wood from a tree with her jaws, chewing it and mixing it with saliva. The first stage in building is a flat foundation on the under-side of a roof or branch. From this grows a short stalk that holds the main part of the nest—the brood cells which make up the spherical comb.

Family planning

Sometimes in warmer regions several queens combine to build a nest and lay eggs, but eventually one queen asserts her authority and the others stop laying. If, however, the senior queen dies, one of the others will take her place. The ovaries of the lesser queens are small in comparison with those

are left to tend the next generation. The larvae are fed on a paste of caterpillars and other insects that have been chewed up by the adults. The larvae grow fat on this diet and after a few weeks the entrances of their cells are sealed with a thin layer of paper and pupation takes place. After emerging from their cells the new workers take a meal from other workers then start their life's work of raising new generations. The nest gradually increases as new cells are added, but in autumn larvae start to die, probably because of a failing food supply, and the colony dies off. Before this happens the males and queens will have set out on their mating flights. The colonies cannot survive in temperate regions as wasps do not store food as honey bees do. In the tropics and near tropics, however, the workers can hibernate through the brief period of bad weather and then become active again.

◁ *Hibernation between mango tree leaves; female S. African wasps* **Polistes fastidiosus.**

△ *An untimely end. A Jamaican paper wasp is killed by an insect-attacking fungus which grows inside the wasp's body until the wasp dies and the fruiting fungus bursts out.*

Cup-shaped nests

The life of the paper wasp is very easy to study because the nest is built above the ground, it is open so that all the activities can be watched and the colony is compara-tively small. Some nests may number up to 500 wasps but there are usually less than 100. In small nests it is quite easy to mark all wasps with individual paint marks and to watch and record their behaviour.

In tropical regions the nests survive the year round but in temperate climates the workers and males die in the autumn, leaving the queens to survive the winter by lying dormant in a shelter. In the following spring the queens emerge and seek a suit-able place for their nests. As the nests are open the site must not be exposed to strong winds or strong sunlight. A common place for nests is under eaves of houses and sheds, or on branches, but as these places

of the senior queen, but if they do lay eggs she destroys them. The senior queen is also looked after more carefully by the workers than the other queens. How she manages to dominate the nest is not really known but it is probably by means of pheromones, chem-icals given off from her body which affect the behaviour and body functions of the other paper wasps.

The queens are fertilised before their winter retreat and the sperms are stored until the eggs are laid. The workers develop from fertilised eggs, but are infertile them-selves because they are reared on a reduced diet. Only later in the season are new queens raised by feeding larvae on a rich diet. At the same time males are reared from unfertilised eggs.

The first batch of larvae are reared by the queens but once they have emerged from cocoons as fully fledged worker wasps they

Cuckoo wasps

The life of social insects—bees, wasps and ants—is a hard one and individual workers do not live long. The ways of these insects have been held up as shining examples of industry, but some species let the side down, and exploit the industry of their relatives. A few species of paper wasps and of the genus *Vespula,* are called cuckoo wasps. The details of their habits are not fully known but it appears that the queens emerge from hibernation after those of the normal species. Each one searches for a flourishing nest and lays her own eggs in it. During this time the reigning queen and the lesser queens as well as the queen larvae and pupae are killed. The cuckoo wasp eggs develop into males and females only, never workers, and these are raised by the host workers to maturity, when they fly off to mate.

The paper nest world of the paper wasp

JAL Cooke

phylum	**Arthropoda**
class	**Insecta**
order	**Hymenoptera**
family	**Vespidae**
genus & species	*Polistes annularis* *P. gallicus* others

*The queen paper wasp builds the small globular nest from paper which she makes by rasping wood from a tree and mixing it with saliva. The nest of **P. smithii** a S. African species (right) contains larvae at various stages and pupae in the capped cells. The wasp on the right is chewing a piece of caterpillar to feed to the larvae. (Above) Another paper wasp tends one of its cells (11 × natural size).*

Papuan turtle

Very few specimens of this freshwater turtle have ever been collected and it is the only living species of its family. Its anatomy is interesting because it is a link between the soft-shelled tortoises of the family Trionychidae and the other cryptodire tortoises, those that withdraw their heads vertically. It is also a relict of a family that once lived in Europe, Asia and North America.

The maximum recorded length of a Papuan turtle is 19 in. Its carapace rises to a peak like the roof of a house while the plastron is flat. The front part of the plastron is connected to the rear portion by stout connective tissue but the shell cannot be closed over the head as in mud turtles (p 1529). The shell is bony and hard but lacks the horny plates that cover the shells of all other tortoises and turtles except the soft-shelled tortoises. The head has a long snout with two tubular nostrils and sharp horny cutting edges on the jaws. The limbs are paddle-like, similar to those of sea turtles. The third, fourth and fifth fingers are long but the short first and second fingers have strong claws. The skin is grey-brown and soft and the blood vessels are faintly discernible through it.

Papuan turtles are confined to the lowlands of southern New Guinea and have been found in only a few parts of this region. As so little collecting has been done in New Guinea it is difficult to know whether the Papuan turtle really is rare.

Not active

Nothing is known of the breeding habits of the Papuan turtle but it is thought that the only time it ever comes on land is to lay eggs. The rest of its life is spent in water. Most specimens have been found in the brackish water of estuaries but some have been found farther up rivers and in lakes. The flippers and the light, streamlined body suggest that Papuan turtles are active swimmers living in open water, but they are found in shallow water near the bottom and one of the functions of the strong, broad claws is to anchor the turtle to a rock or log. The claws are also used to hold prey that cannot be swallowed whole. While the food is held firm pieces can be bitten off by the jaws. In captivity Papuan turtles have fed on lettuce and apples, meat, worms, pond snails and young mice. Live fishes were ignored, which supports the idea that Papuan turtles are sluggish and feed only on plants, slow-moving animals and carrion.

Underwater breathing

At intervals a Papuan turtle leaves the bottom and swims steeply to the water surface to breathe, but like other aquatic tortoises and turtles it gets a fair proportion of its oxygen from the water. It may be that it does this partly through its skin since blood vessels can be seen near the surface of the soft skin. Moreover, when lifted from the water a Papuan turtle expels water from its cloaca, so exchange of oxygen and other gases could take place in the hind part of the intestine, as happens in some fishes. It also seems likely that the mouth is a site for gas exchange, just as some fishes and frogs use the lining of the mouth as a sort of lung. While the turtle is resting on the bottom the throat can be seen pumping about 24 times each minute. Water is drawn in through a gap between the jaws and is ejected through the nose and mouth. This water current may also enhance the sense of smell as chemicals will be drawn through the nose. These ideas are partly conjectural and will not be made certain until more Papuan turtles are kept in captivity.

△ *Rare or not? Very few specimens of this freshwater turtle have ever been collected.*

Fixing the reward

Collecting rare animals is often simplified by offering local people a reward for specimens. There are drawbacks, however. The story was recounted on page 799 of how the supposedly rare Madagascan fly was found in swarms on a native cow; and in England a zoologist living in a seaside town in the 1880's offered a reward for each specimen of a small sponge called a sea orange, which he thought was rare. The next day a barrel packed with 1 in. sea oranges arrived at his door. But the search for Papuan turtles took an opposite turn to these embarrassing events. A German collector once managed to bring live Papuan turtles back to Europe. On arriving at a small village in Papua he had offered a reward for live Papuan turtles. In due course a number of turtles were brought in, but none was a Papuan turtle. One day a villager told the collector, quite incidentally, that he had a long-nosed turtle that was especially good to eat. The collector realised his mistake. He was offering too low a price for turtles that were worth more as food, so he increased his reward sufficiently to overcome the villagers' desire for turtle meat and in a few days had collected nine live specimens. The moral of these stories is that animals not well known to scientists may be well known to the local people, but care must be taken when trying to get hold of them.

class	**Reptilia**
order	**Chelonia**
family	**Carettochelidae**
genus & species	*Carettochelys insculpta*

Paradise fish

This is the fish that first made tropical aquarium keeping popular. People have been keeping goldfish for a long time but it was in the mid-19th century that home aquaria became the rage. At first marine animals and a few freshwater fishes were kept in them. Then in 1861, the paradise fish was brought to Paris. Before long it had reached England and other European countries and in 1876 it was taken to the United States. At first aquarists were afraid the new fish would injure their goldfish. But in fact it was the paradise fish that started the fashion of keeping 'tropicals'.

The paradise fish can be up to 3½ in. long and has a body that is flattened from side to side. It has flowing dorsal and anal fins, a large rounded tail, small pectoral fins and pelvic fins about the same size as the pectorals and lying beneath them. The male is brown to greenish-grey with marbling on the head and a large blackish spot ringed with orange on each gill cover. The flanks are banded blue-green and carmine. The fins are reddish, the pelvics white-tipped and the dorsal and anal fins have dark spots. The female is similar but paler.

The range of the paradise fish is from Korea through eastern China, including Formosa, to South Vietnam. A second species, the round-tailed paradise fish, similar but slightly smaller, has much the same range but does not go so far south. A third species, also small, with two longitudinal bands on the flanks, ranges from India and Ceylon, through Burma to South Vietnam.

Gene Wolfsheimer

Wild or tame

Much has been written about the paradise fish in scientific and aquarist journals, discussing two aspects of it: whether it is the wild form or one bred by the Chinese, and what is the purpose of its bubble nest. No firm conclusions have been reached. On the whole it seems that the fish as we know it in the aquarium is much the same as the fish that is wild in the rice fields. The aquarium breeds have been only slightly altered from the wild forms although there are also special breeds. There is, for example, a dark variety, *concolor*, and there is an albino strain, white with pink eyes and pink bands on the flanks which breeds true.

Bubble blowers unlimited

As in many other labyrinth fishes, paradise fishes build nests of bubbles. The male blows out bubbles of air and mucus which rise to the surface and there form a raft. Then follows an elaborate mating. The colours of the male become brighter as the breeding period draws near, the female becomes paler. When the female is about to spawn the male wraps himself round her while she lies in the normal position just under the bubble raft. As the eggs begin to be laid

the pair make a barrel roll, which brings the female upside-down with the male still wrapped round her, so he fertilises the eggs as they leave her body. Then he releases the female and trembles for a few seconds before gathering any slowly sinking eggs in his mouth, rising to the underside of the bubble nest and spitting the eggs onto it. Unlike other bubble nesters whose eggs are heavier than water, those of the paradise fish mostly float upwards when laid. Only a small percentage fail to do this and slowly sink. When the clutch is complete he blows more bubbles to make a second layer under the eggs, sealing them in. This may be repeated time and time again.

There are several opinions about the purpose of the raft. One is that it protects the eggs from the heat of strong sunlight beating down on the rice fields. Another is that it shades them from strong light. A third is that it protects the eggs from bacteria. The fourth suggestion, and the most likely, is that it keeps the eggs together, and also the fry when they hatch, making it easier for the male to guard them. The eggs hatch in 2 days at a temperature of 26°C/80°F.

Paradise fish can respond to sounds of frequencies between 2 637 and 4 699 cycles per second and there is the possibility that they make sounds, perhaps inaudible to us, which stimulate breeding.

Reason in their quarrelsome habits

Little is known about the enemies of paradise fish in the wild. More is known about their pugnacious nature in aquaria, where they will tear the fins of other kinds of fishes if placed in a mixed tank. They feed on any small animals, being very predatory, and they readily attack members of their own kind. In aquaria care must be taken to keep male and female apart until they are ready to breed, and it may happen that, after mating, the female may be savaged by the male if she has too little

△ *Fashion makers—paradise fish made tropical aquaria popular. Species:* **Macropodus dayi.**

space to get away from him. What purpose is served by this internecine strife is hard to say. Perhaps clues can be found from experimental work that has been carried out on paradise fish in the laboratory. It has been found that they eat more food when grouped together but grow faster when placed in tanks on their own. Their aggressiveness may be purely a matter of keeping each fish spaced out, to give them growing space, or it may be a natural means of controlling numbers.

Females take over

Although the building of the bubble nest and care of the young is normally the work of the male, females have been seen to do both. Presumably, should a male be killed after the eggs are laid a female can take over his work. That, however, cannot be the whole story. In aquaria females ready to lay but having no male present will build a bubble raft and lay their eggs, unfertilised. It has even been known for such a female to be helped by another female. In one instance an aquarium keeper kept a male and female apart, by sliding a sheet of glass between them. The male started to build a bubble raft one side of the glass and the female started one the other side. When the aquarist noticed this, and before he could move the glass, the female had laid her eggs under the raft and was trying to keep the male, on the other side of the glass, at bay.

class	**Pisces**
order	**Perciformes**
family	**Anabantidae**
genus & species	*Macropodus opercularis* others

*Peculiar puzzling pseudid—the paradoxical frog has long been a zoological problem as it has no close relatives and so is difficult to classify. It is now put in its own family Pseudidae. This species, **Pseudis paradoxa** is the largest and best known paradoxical frog so called because of the disproportion in size between the tadpole and adult. It seems unbelievable that a 10½in. tadpole could metamorphose into a 1½in. froglet, but this is what happens.*

Paradoxical frog

These frogs are quite the reverse of other frogs: at metamorphosis they are several times smaller than their tadpoles.

In outward appearance the paradoxical frog looks like any ordinary frog. It is up to 3 in. long. Its hindfeet are webbed but the toes project beyond the webbing more than usual. Its colour varies among the usual greens and browns with darker spots and blotches but the hindlegs have a harlequin colouring of yellow and black.

There are several sub-species, the best known living on the island of Trinidad and in the northeastern area of South America and in part of the Amazon basin. Others are found in other parts of South America as far south as northern Argentina.

Stirring up mud

Paradoxical frogs are usually heard and not seen. They seldom come onto land and whenever they come to the surface of the water, they usually expose just their eyes or nostrils, and these are usually hidden among small water plants crowding the surface. The moment they are disturbed they dive. They have an added protection: their skin is unusually slippery so they are extremely hard to hold. They often make coughing grunts, however, almost like pigs.

Another peculiarity is that the toes have an extra joint, which gives them greater length, and this is linked with the method of feeding. They stir up the mud at the bottom of shallow lakes to find the small mud-dwelling invertebrates which they feed on. The first toe on each forefoot is opposable to the others, and it is used as a thumb for grasping food.

From giant to dwarf

The outstanding feature of this frog is the size of the tadpole, which may be 10½ in. long. When it changes into a froglet it shrinks to 1½ in. This is so unusual that the first scientists to study these frogs could not believe they belonged to the same species. When the tadpole shrinks by this tremendous amount all the internal organs must shrink proportionately, which was quite unheard of, so the adult frog was given one scientific name and the tadpole was given another. Only when the actual change from one to another had been observed was it realized that only one species was involved. In fact, the whole process was so puzzling that for a time there were several different scientific names for the different stages in the life-history. This is not the only time such a thing has happened, but it is very rare for there to be such a great reduction in size from the young or larval animal to the adult. It raises all manner of questions to which we do not yet know the answers; for example, how large the eggs are and whether they contain large quantities of yolk to feed the growing tadpole in its early stages. Another question to which we would like the answer is what advantage there can be in a tadpole growing so large then shrinking so much as it turns into a froglet.

Tadpoles to market

One reason why information on these frogs is so scanty is that they are difficult to find and therefore to keep in sufficient numbers in captivity to study them. Three individuals of one species were collected 100 years ago but there is no record of its having been seen since. Within the last few years, however, South American zoologists have been finding more of other species in areas south of the Amazon Basin, so more information may soon begin to trickle through. The tadpoles are easier to catch as they can be netted but even this apparently is not simple. The local Indians catch the tadpoles, as well as the adults, on hooks baited with grasshoppers, then sell them in the markets, and the tadpoles are particularly relished.

class	**Amphibia**
order	**Salientia**
family	**Pseudidae**
genus & species	***Pseudis paradoxa***

*Frog that shrinks as it grows, the paradoxical frog **Pseudis paradoxa**. An entirely aquatic frog, it lives in remote swamps and marshes where it is nearly invisible among the water weeds.*

Recorded distribution, although the frog probably has a wider unrecorded distribution.

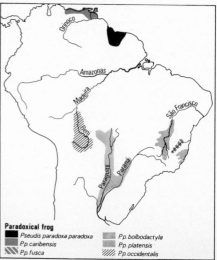

Paradoxical frog
- Pseudis paradoxa paradoxa
- P.p.caribensis
- P.p.fusca
- P.p.bolbodactyla
- P.p.platensis
- P.p.occidentalis

Lorus & Margery Milne

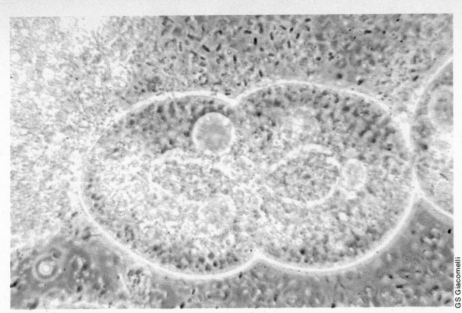

rows. These cilia are essentially the same as those that line our own breathing tubes and are associated with an orderly arrangement of structures just below the surface. The covering, or pellicle, is uniform except in the gullet and is made up of a lattice of polygons (usually hexagons) in close-packed rows just under the outer membrane. From the centre of each emerges one cilium, or two in **P. bursaria**, and at the base of each cilium is a cylindrical 'basal body'. To the left of each row of basal bodies, and connected to them, is a fine fibre which could be involved in coordinating the beating of the cilia. Many of the details are only revealed by electron microscopy and some of the earlier pictures, still being reproduced, are wrong. Amongst the cilia, just under

◁ *Binary fission in* **P. putrinum** *(× 1 000).*
▽ *Final stage, the furrow deepens (× 1 000).*

Paramecium

Nearly 6 000 species of ciliate Protista have been described. They are single-celled animals that typically, though not always, feed and swim by means of cilia. If any of these can be described as well-known, it is surely the much-studied slipper animalcule **Paramecium** *described by Christian Huygens as long ago as 1678 when microscopy was in its infancy. The largest are about $\frac{1}{3}$ mm long and the smallest about $\frac{1}{6}$ of that. There are about 10 species differing in size, shape and other details, but they are all elongated and more or less rounded at the ends and each has a wide shallow groove on its side, leading into a blind gullet. The general appearance is aptly expressed in the old popular name of 'slipper animal-cule'.* **Paramecium** *does not change its shape like* **Amoeba** *(p 34) except when squeezing through holes, and it swims with its short cilia arranged in longitudinal*

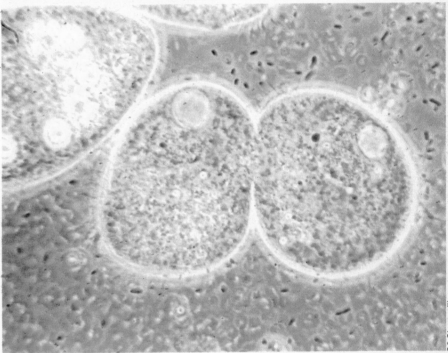

◁ *There are about 10 different species of* **Paramecium**, *2 of which are shown here (× 680).*

the surface, are little carrot-shaped bodies called trichocysts. Each one can discharge a rod $\frac{1}{50} - \frac{1}{25}$ mm long and ending in a sharp tip. It is not clear if these have any offensive or defensive function.

Inside the body there are two kinds of nucleus: a large 'macronucleus' and one or more small 'micronuclei'. For bailing out excess water, there are contractile vacuoles. In **P. caudatum,** the most widespread species, there is one at each end and the two contract alternately, but in other species there may be only one, or there may be as many as seven. Around each contractile vacuole are several radial canals which gradually fill with fluid, before discharging into the central vacuole, which collapses as it discharges its contents.

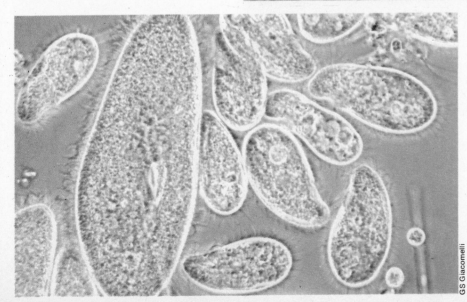

Trial-and-error navigation

In swimming the cilia of paramecium are co-ordinated, each beating a little in advance of the one behind it in the line, so that waves seem to pass from the front to the rear. As the body moves through the water it rotates anticlockwise, as seen from behind. When it meets an obstruction or an unfavourable chemical, the cilia beat in the opposite direction so the animal backs, then it turns and advances again, repeating this until a clear path is found. It is largely by this simple process of trial and error, that individuals tend to remain within the most favourable regions of their environment. Recently it has been shown that the reverse beating, when the front end is touched, is brought about by a temporary increase in the permeability of the surface to calcium ions and that stimulation of the rear end causes faster swimming by an increase in the permeability of the surface to potassium ions. The two reactions are accompanied by changes in the voltage across the surface of the animal.

Sometimes paramecium loses much of the organization of its body and surrounds itself with a thick membrane which becomes angular like a sand grain. This formation of a cyst probably aids dispersion and survival during a period of drought, but it has not often been seen.

Though some species occur in brackish water, paramecium lives mainly in fresh water, particularly where there is abundant decaying organic matter and its attendant bacteria. It is easily cultured in infusions of hay.

Temporary feeding organs

Paramecium eats bacteria, minute algae and smaller Protista wafted into the gullet by the cilia of the oral groove. The food is propelled down the gullet by more cilia, some of which are joined together side by side in rows to form 'undulating membranes'. At the bottom of the gullet, the food is collected in vacuoles in the cytoplasm. These tiny cavities then move into the cytoplasm and follow a definite path around the inside of the animal, finally discharging their indigestible contents at a point on the surface. If paramecium is fed on dried milk stained with a dye called congo red, the dye can be seen changing colour as the food vacuole moves around, showing that it is being subjected first to acid conditions and then alkaline, like food in our own digestive tracts. One species *P. bursaria* is coloured green by the cells of an alga *Chlorella* that lives inside it. Presumably, both organisms benefit from the partnership.

Sex at its simplest

Most of the time paramecium reproduces by division. The oral groove disappears, the nuclei divide, new contractile vacuoles form and a furrow appears across the middle of the body. In addition to this process of binary fission, which may happen 1–5 times a day, there occurs less frequently and often shortly after a depletion of food, a form of sexual reproduction usually referred to as conjugation. In *P. caudatum*, which has one of each kind of nucleus, the two individuals come together, joining in the regions of their oral grooves. The macronuclei break

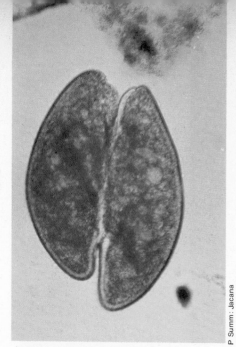

P Summ : Jacana

△ *Paramecium* can reproduce in two ways, by an asexual method called binary fission, shown overleaf, in which the animal merely splits into two new individuals; or by a sexual method called conjugation, shown here, in which two animals come together and exchange nuclear materials so producing offspring with different hereditary constituents (× 650).

down and in each individual the micronucleus divides into four. Of these four, three degenerate while the other divides again so each individual has 2 micronuclei, each with half the usual number of chromosomes. One of these migrates across into the other individual and there fuses with its opposite number. After this exchange of genetic material the two animals separate and the single effective nucleus in each divides again three times to give 8 nuclei

▽ *Pond water life, this is just a sample of what can be seen under the microscope. Among the freshwater algae and plankton are two paramecia, **P. aurelia**. They are easily distinguished by their characteristic slipper-shaped bodies. Free-swimming ciliates, they move by beating the cilia that cover their bodies (× 210).*

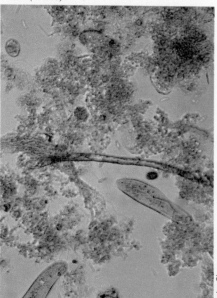

John Clegg

from which are formed the micro- and macronuclei of 4 new individuals. Sometimes self-fertilisation occurs: the 2 animals come together but do not exchange nuclei. In other instances, self-fertilisation takes place without mating. There are no distinct males and females, but each species occurs in a number of varieties and each variety in more than one 'mating type': conjugation can only occur between members of different mating types.

Killer strains

The nuclei in paramecium, as in other animals and plants, contain DNA, the complex chemical in which the information essential for form and function is coded, and which is transferred from one generation to the next during reproduction. In reproduction by binary fission the nucleus simply divides and there is no rearrangement of DNA, each offspring inheriting the same genetic information as the other. In sexual reproduction the exchange of half the genetic material allows for a rearrangement of DNA so the offspring vary slightly from the parents. This variation allows for evolution, the variants best suited to the environment surviving. In reproduction by binary fission, however, it is not just this genetic information that is passed to the progeny, but also the cytoplasm. Structures and characters can therefore be passed on from generation to generation other than in the nuclei. This is most dramatically seen in the phenomenon of 'killer' and 'sensitive' strains of *P. aurelia*. Certain strains, known as killers, contain kappa particles in their cytoplasm which release toxins into the water which cause members of other 'sensitive' strains to die in a few hours after showing such symptoms as paralysis, spinning and the appearance of a hump on the body. Sensitives can, however, be mated to killers without harm, provided suitable precautions are taken. If the pair remain together for a few minutes only, the two continue as before, killer and sensitive, but as a result of mating they acquire the same genetic make-up as far as the nuclei are concerned. If, however, the pair remain together for longer, for example half an hour, some cytoplasm is exchanged in addition to the nuclei and then both become killers. It is the kappa particles which pass over in the cytoplasm and are responsible for the effect, but just what the particles are is not clear, though they might be akin to viruses. They contain DNA and if destroyed by high temperatures or X-rays, killers are turned into sensitives. There is, however, more than one kind of killer race and, in some, a certain nuclear gene must be present if the particles are to be inherited.

phylum	**Protista**
class	**Ciliata**
subclass	**Holotricha**
order	**Hymenostomatida**
suborder	**Peniculina**
family	**Parameciidae**
genus	*Paramecium*

Parrakeet

Parrakeets are members of the parrot family, the most well known of which is the budgerigar (p 297). It is very difficult to give a definition of the name parrakeet, practically every book on birds, and certainly all dictionaries, differ in their views. Even the spelling of the name varies, from paroquet to parroquet, parakeet and parrakeet. Generally speaking, parrakeets can be defined as small brightly coloured parrots with long tails, but the name has been given to many genera and species in tropical America as well as in southern and southeast Asia and Australasia. Moreover, many of these have the alternative name of conure and rosella, the latter being a well known type of Australian parrot. To make matters worse many have more than one common name. The only hope of sorting out this confusion is to go to a book by AA Prestwich, the Secretary of the Avicultural Society of Great Britain, with the title 'I Name This Parrot . . .' In this the author has listed all the members of the parrot family, with their common names as well as their scientific names. The parrakeets he names belong to 23 genera, 68 species and 128 subspecies. In addition the parrakeets known as conures belong to 7 genera, 46 species and 63 sub-species. Since every species or sub-species of parrakeet has its own particular common name, this means in effect that there are 191 kinds of parrakeet known to aviculturalists, and since some have more than one common name this gives us about 300 names to play with.

New World parrakeets

Identification in this large group of colourful little parrots is especially confusing as they are not all closely related. The American parrakeets or conures, ranging from Mexico to Paraguay are related to the macaws, differing from them in having the lores—that is the space on each side of the head between the beak and the eye—feathered and in having a large swollen beak, not compressed as in the macaws. Also, the fourth feather of the wing is long and narrow and the nostrils are exposed. These parrakeets are usually some shade of green, yellow or orange with blue on the wings and red on the head and breast. The slender-billed parrakeet is another American species. It is 15 in. long and has pale green plumage with crimson on the forehead and around the eyes and lores and a faint patch on the abdomen. It lives in Chile, in large flocks numbering hundreds, and although it keeps mainly to the forests the slender-billed parrakeet comes out to attack crops from October to April, feeding on cereal crops and the roots of grass. The grey-breasted parrakeet is green with grey on the head, throat and breast. It is nearly

▷ *Looking over his shoulder from his lofty perch, a green ringnecked parrakeet.*

Peter Jackson: Photo Res

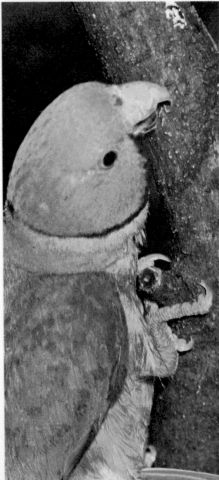

△ Unruly chicks mob their parent for food.
The torquoisine or western rock parrakeet nests
in crevices among rocks.
◁ Multicoloured and broad-tailed, an eastern
rosella **Platycercus eximius**.
▽ Uphill all the way, a blossom-headed
parrakeet climbs with its feet and beak.

a foot long and ranges from Bolivia to Argentine. There are several related species in South America. Some of the smaller American species are the green parrakeets, 7−10 in. long, found in northern South America and Central America.

Old World parrakeets

The Old World parrakeets are more nearly related to the true parrots. They also are mainly green. The ringnecked parrakeet of Africa, up to 1½ ft long, has a graduated tail in which the two central feathers are long and narrow. It has a notch in the upper half of the beak and a rose-coloured collar. The Indian blossom-headed parrakeet, a near relative, is more handsome still with the head of the male tinged with red, plum-coloured cheeks and a black collar.

Australian parrakeets

In southern Australia and Tasmania live the grass parrakeets, of which the lovely torquoisine is the best known. They are less than a foot long and half of this is tail, and are mainly green with blue in the wings and blue sometimes in the tail. Normally they move about in parties of 6−8 but will come together in large flocks as particular seeds ripen. There are related species in New Zealand and some of the islands of the southwest Pacific. Also in the southwest Pacific, New Caledonia and the Loyalty Islands are the ground parrakeets. These are up to 14 in. long, and usually have a crest. The New Caledonia crested parrakeet has a crest of two black feathers tipped with red but in others it is made up of six feathers which are usually green.

The ground parrakeets of Australia are of two kinds, long-tailed and short-tailed. The first are sometimes spoken of as swamp parrakeets because they tend to roost in trees in swamps. They are distinguished by the alternating dark and light bars on the tail feathers which has led to a further common name, pheasant-cuckoo. The long-tailed ground parrakeets are about a foot long of which half is tail. The general colour is green, with orange on the forehead and the body plumage mottled with bands of black and yellow. The short-tailed parra-keets are nocturnal, coming out at sunset to feed, and are sometimes called night parra-keets. They are now rare and there are fears they may be on the way to extinction.

Topsy-turvy slumber

Parrakeets usually roost in trees and the hanging parrakeets sleep head downwards like bats. It seems that many more parra-keets than are realised sleep like this. One is the lineolated parrakeet which feeds at twilight. By day it is quiescent, freezing for long periods at a time. At other times it may perch lengthways along a branch, nightjar fashion.

Vegetarians all

Some parrakeets go about in parties of half a dozen or so, others in flocks of hundreds, even thousands at times. They feed in trees or on the ground, the proportion of time given to each varying with the species. Their food is mainly seeds, fruits, leaves and flowers, and where they are numerous they are apt to be a menace to crops.

Devoted families

Their nests are usually in hollows in trees or among rocks, with no more than rotten wood litter on which to lay their eggs. The grey-breasted parrakeet is unusual in build-ing a nest in the branches of a tree. Several may nest close together, each nest made of a mass of sticks, roofed in and with an entrance to one side, high up in a tall tree. Both female and male build the nest but the hen alone incubates the eggs, which is usual among parrakeets, and the male attends her and guards the nest. The number of eggs varies from 4 to 10 with the species. Incubation usually lasts a month or more, but may be much less in some species. The chicks remain in the nest for 4−5 weeks, or as much as 10 weeks, both parents feeding them.

Carolina parrakeet

A famous bird is the Carolina parrakeet. It used to be seen in large numbers from South Virginia to Texas and southeast to Flor-ida. It is gaily coloured in green, rose, yellow and white, but its raucous calling as it flies about attracts attention as much as its colour. It made a good pet, so it was in demand as a cage bird, and its flesh was good eating. Its feathers made good adorn-ments for hats. At the same time it was des-tructive to fruit and cereal crops. If one was shot its companions flew off but re-turned again and again to the spot, as if trying to rescue it. By the 1880's it was becoming rare. There may still be a few Carolina parrakeets in some out-of-the-way spot, but this is probably a vain hope.

class	**Aves**
order	**Psittaciformes**
family	**Psittacidae**
genera & species	***Aratinga*** *spp conures*
	Brotogeris tirica
	green parrakeet
	Conuropsis carolinensis
	Carolina parrakeet
	Enicognathus leptorhynchus
	slender-billed parrakeet
	Eunymphicus cornutus
	crested parrakeet
	Geopsittacus occidentalis
	night parrakeet
	Myiopsitta monachus
	grey-breasted parrakeet
	Neophema pulchella
	torquoisine
	Pezoporus wallicus
	ground parrakeet
	Psittacula cyanocephala
	blossom-headed parrakeet
	P. krameri
	ringnecked parrakeet, others

▷ *What is in a name? According to the dictionary a parrakeet is a small, especially long-tailed, kind of parrot. Not altogether very helpful but this bird with its technicolored plumage perching coquettishly among the sunshine-yellow Australian wattle is a crimson parrakeet or rosella, perhaps better known as* **Platycercus elegans** *to save confusion.*

Parrot profile. The African grey parrot, the most sought after and finest talking bird. The males make better mimics than the females. An admirable pet, it is reputed to have lived for 80 years in captivity. In the wild it travels in flocks feeding on all kinds of fruits and seeds testing them first with its fleshy tongue.

Parrot

Only about a third of the 315 members of the parrot family are given the name 'parrot'. The rest have other names, like cockatoos, parrakeets, lories, lorikeets, and macaws. Of the 107 parrots, 25 are amazons, stout-bodied American birds with mainly green plumage and short, square or rounded tails. One of the largest is the yellow-headed amazon which is 15 in. long. It is green except for the head and some blue and red in the wings. It ranges from Mexico to Brazil. One of the smallest is the white-fronted amazon which is 10 in. long. This amazon has a white forehead and bright red lores, and the male has a red wing patch. Another typical parrot is the African grey of the forests of tropical West and Central Africa. This bird has white cheeks and a red tail.

All members of the parrot family have large heads, short necks and strongly hooked beaks with the upper mandible longer than the lower and curving downwards. There is a broad cere at the base of the beak through which the nostrils open. Of the four toes on each foot two are directed forwards, two backwards. Powder down feathers are scattered through the plumage.

Raucous and agile

Parrots are essentially forest dwellers, travelling about in noisy flocks, the smaller parrots twittering, the larger uttering raucous shrieks and squawks. They climb about the trees, using beaks as well as feet, and, unlike most other birds, they can hold food with one foot. Their food is fruits, seeds and nuts. They seem to have a more highly developed sense of taste than most birds and will test food with their fleshy tongues before beginning to eat it.

Vocal mimics

The amazons and the African grey have been favourite pets, especially the latter, for centuries. This is because of their being able to 'talk', and the main interest in parrots lies in their vocal mimicry. A good 'talker' will imitate almost any sound from the songs of other birds and mechanical sounds to human speech. It will whistle tunes, sing short phrases from songs, laugh, cry, even call people by name: in short express itself vocally in a remarkably human way. An African grey has been recorded as imitating actions, using the foot to imitate its owner's use of the hand.

Where no wild parrots talk
The reputation of parrots as talkers has suffered in recent years from claims that budgerigars, and also mynahs, are superior in this respect. It is, however, doubtful whether there is much to choose between all three. It has also been repeatedly said that a parrot 'has no idea what it is saying'. In fact, careful study shows that parrots associate words and sounds with events and persons in much the same way, and to much the same degree, as a child of 2 years of age. Another assertion often made is that although such good mimics when tamed parrots never imitate sounds in the wild. This is hard to believe. A tame European jay is also a good talker and wild jays have been recorded as imitating the hoot of an owl. Such records are few but more would be made if people went out of their way to listen for them. It is highly likely that parrots also mimic sounds in the wild but that nobody has gone to the trouble of making the particular study needed to prove the point.

Cavity nesters
The breeding habits of parrots are fairly uniform. They usually nest in cavities in trees but some use burrows in the ground or crevices in rocks. A few Australian parrots dig holes in termite mounds. The nesting cavity is not lined; at best the eggs are laid on the powder of rotten wood or similar material. The eggs are nearly spherical, white and somewhat glossy. The clutch varies from 2 to 3 in the larger species to 10 in the smaller species. Few details are known except from parrots in aviaries, and the later events are best typified by what is known of the African grey. In this species the eggs are laid at intervals of 3 days, usually 4 eggs forming a clutch. Incubation, by the hen alone, lasts just over a month. The newly hatched chick is flesh-coloured with a light beak and light claws. The body soon becomes covered with a light down and the beak turns black after a few days. The hen broods the chicks, especially at night, for 2 months. Meanwhile, the male shares the feeding of the nestlings, by regurgitation. When first fledged the young parrot is like the parent except that the body feathers are a darker and softer grey, the tail feathers are a less vivid red and the eye is entirely black.

Birds as ventriloquists

When we consider how a bird's voice box is made the fact that they can imitate such a wide range of sounds is quite remarkable. Our larynx, with its vocal cords, is near the top of the windpipe. Air passing across the vocal cords makes them vibrate and the

sounds so produced are modified to form words and other modulated sounds by altering the position of the tongue and the teeth and by changing the shape of the cheeks and lips. In a bird the voice box or syrinx is at the base of the windpipe and it is worked by a dozen small muscles to produce all the modifications of the sounds. There are no cheeks or lips, in the sense of our pliable cheeks and lips, there are no teeth and the tongue is less mobile. So a bird must produce all the sounds it makes down in the

Looking down from his treetop perch is the blue-fronted amazon, **Amazona aestiva**. The amazon is another favourite pet, rivalling the African grey parrot for its famous talking ability.

throat. That is why a bird can sing, and often does, with the beak closed. It is also why a parrot can talk with its beak closed or nearly so. The ventriloquist does something like this, so producing the illusion that the voice is coming from somewhere else. The calls of many birds are often described as ventriloquial.

If we listen carefully to a ventriloquist we find his consonants are badly formed, although they sound right to the casual ear. It is the same with talking birds. This is underlined by the following story of a dog living in a house where there was a parrot. Whenever the dog rushed out into the garden, when it should not, its owner would whistle it or call it by name. The dog would

stop in its headlong rush and return to the house. If the dog rushed out when its owner was not there the parrot would whistle it or call it by name in what seemed a perfect imitation of the owner's whistle and voice. The dog, on hearing this, would raise its ears to listen, but without turning its head the slightest, then drop them again, meanwhile continuing its headlong run. It was as if the dog were saying to itself: 'Oh, it's only the parrot.' The assumption is that the dog, with its more discriminating ears, could *immediately* tell the difference between the owner's voice and the parrot's—which is more than human beings could do.

class	**Aves**		
order	**Psittaciformes**		
family	**Psittacidae**		
genera & species	**Amazona albifrons** *white-fronted amazon* **A. ochrocephala** *yellow-headed amazon* **Psittacus erithacus** *African grey* *others*		

1669

Fowkein grey headed crow-tit, **Paradoxornis gularis:** *a grand name for such a small bird. Parrotbills are titlike birds with a deep, short, heavy bill like that of a parrot's.*

Parrotbill

These small titlike birds are aptly named: they have a short, deep convex bill, like a parrot's. They are also known as crow tits or suthoras, and are classed by some ornithologists with the tits and by others with the babblers. Most of the 19 or 20 species live in the Orient, from India to China but not in the Malayan region. The reedling, however, ranges from China to Britain, where it breeds in a few areas mainly on the east coast. This species is usually called the bearded tit, the male having a prominent black stripe on each side of the bill like drooping moustaches. It is about 6½ in. long with a 3in. tail and in general appearance it looks rather like a small, long-tailed sparrow and can be confused with a long-tailed tit. The plumage is generally light brown with stripes of black, white and brown on the wings. The bill is yellow and the head lavender-grey. The female's plumage is dull by comparison.

A little larger than the reedling is Gould's parrotbill, 7 in. long, brown above and whitish below with black patches around the eyes. Blyth's parrotbill is only 4 in. long.

Agile acrobats
Parrotbills clamber agilely among grasses and bamboos in a very titlike manner pausing straddled between two stems. The habits of many of them are hardly known but most live in groups of up to 50, some-times in company with other birds such as tits and babblers, foraging in tall grasses, bamboos or the lower levels of trees, where their constant chattering gives them away. The reedling lives in reed beds where its presence is first betrayed by its high-pitched calls. Often all that will be seen of it is a glimpse of a small dark bird disappearing into the depths of the reeds but in the autumn especially small groups can be seen flying quite high over the reeds or foraging or roosting together among the reeds.

Stripping reeds
Parrotbills feed on insects, grass seeds and sometimes berries. During the breeding season reedlings feed on insects, caterpillars, mayflies and other insects, together with a few small snails. In the winter, however, they feed mainly on the seeds of reeds. The black-fronted parrotbill of Nepal, Burma, Thailand and China feeds on bamboo shoots as well as insects and the reedbed parrotbill feeds on insects and larvae that live inside the stems of reeds. The reedbed parrotbill is restricted to a 50 mile stretch of reeds along the Yangste Kiang, near its mouth. It searches for the holes made in the reeds by insects, then straddles the reed, inserting the tip of the upper mandible and tearing away strips of reed until the insects are exposed. The noise of the reeds being torn apart makes these parrotbills easy to find. They are also easy to approach.

Reed hammocks
Parrotbill nests are made of the leaves of grass or bamboo or strips torn off reeds woven tightly into cups around bamboo or stout grass stems and bound with cobwebs. Reedlings line their nests with the flowers of reeds and a few feathers. Both sexes help in building the nest but the male makes the lining. When he is displaying to the female he fluffs out his moustaches and erects a sort of crest on his head. The pair posture to each other with their tails spread and they fly up together with quivering wings. In captivity the female reedling has been seen roosting under the wing of the male. Reedlings do not hold territories but search for their food over a large area of their reedbed.

The eggs, 2–4 for most parrotbills but 5–7 for reedlings, are incubated for nearly a fortnight by both parents. The chicks stay in the nest for about 10 days. There are 2, sometimes 3, broods a year.

Resilient reedling

The reedling is one of the rarest British breeding birds. At one time it was much more widespread in southern and eastern England, but cutting of reedbeds and drainage of marshes together with the sale of both the eggs and the birds has restricted the range of the reedling until it bred only in the reedbeds of Norfolk and Suffolk and a few other scattered localities. Since the nineteenth century the reedling has been safe from human persecution but it has suffered badly during hard winters. After the long winter of 1916/17 very few reedlings were left. Numbers increased again until 1939/40, when there was another severe winter. Again they recovered until the 6 weeks' hard weather early in 1947. So few reedlings survived the hard winter of 1947 that it was thought they would become extinct in Britain. In the summer of 1947 only 4 breeding pairs were recorded. Yet once again there was a remarkable recovery and 10 years later over 100 pairs were recorded in the counties of Norfolk and Suffolk. Since then numbers have continued to increase, with only temporary setbacks due to bad weather or flooding, and reedlings have now spread to other parts of the country. HE Axell, writing in *British Birds* for 1966, describes how groups of reedlings can be seen leaving the reedbeds after the breeding season. They spread across the country in search of new reedbeds where they can feed, and some stay there to breed. Reedlings have also crossed the North Sea from Holland, to reinforce those already in Britain.

The severe effects of hard winters on the reedling population is due to snow covering the reeds. In 1962-3 the population was not affected as much as in 1947 because although the frost was harder and lasted longer, there was less snow and the reedlings were able to find food.

class	**Aves**
order	**Passeriformes**
family	**Muscicapidae**
genera & species	***Panurus biarmicus*** *reedling* ***Paradoxornis flavirostris*** *Gould's parrotbill* **P. heudei** *reedbed parrotbill* **P. poliotis** *Blyth's parrotbill, others*

Colourful coral fish—parrotfish appear as blue-green patches moving around the tropical reefs on which they feed. With their parrot-like beaks (below) they bite off chunks of coral leaving distinct tooth impressions behind. Because of this feeding habit parrotfish slowly erode the reefs.

Parrotfish

These brilliantly coloured fishes do not in fact get their name from their gaudy colours but from their teeth, which are joined to form a 'parrot's beak' in the front of the mouth. Nobody knows how many species there are: 350 have been named but there are probably fewer than 80.

Parrotfishes live around tropical reefs. They vary in adult size, from 1—6 ft; a few have reached 12 ft. When merely cruising around they swim with their pectoral fins, using their tail only when they need to swim more quickly.

Herds of fishes

Parrotfishes of the genus *Sparisoma* may live solitary lives or they may come together in small groups without any social organisation. Some species of the genus *Scarus* move about in large schools of up to 40 when feeding, rather like herds of cattle. Because of this parrotfish are sometimes referred to as the 'cattle of the sea'. Often they are seen near the shore with their backs out of water. The schools are made up of fishes of about the same size, the smallest keeping together, and similarly with the medium and large sized individuals. In some species of *Scarus* the groups are smaller and are made up of several females with a mature male acting as leader, like cows with a bull. Should another male join the group he is chased away, the boss male sometimes trailing him 20 ft away for a distance of 100 yards before rejoining his harem.

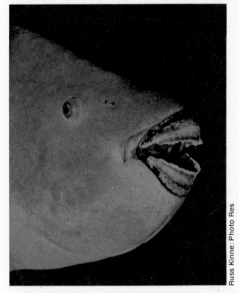

Different coloured sexes

For a long time parrotfishes were separated into species on the basis of colour. Then it was found that the same species could appear in different colours. Some species go through at least three different colour phases in the course of a lifetime. In others there is a marked difference between male and female. For example, *Scarus taeniopterus* is striped with orange and blue while *S. croicensis* is striped brown and white. Then it was realized they both belong to the same species, the first being the male, the second the female. This was tested by taking the female parrotfishes and injecting them with

male sex hormones. *S. croicensis* so injected turned from brown and white striped to orange and blue striped. Where males and females are differently coloured the young fishes are coloured like the females. As they mature the females keep these colours but the males take on the colours of the mature males. Another change that can take place with age, in some parrotfishes, is that the males become bumpheaded. Instead of the forehead sloping it becomes a large bump, so that old males have heavy blunt snouts.

Homing by the sun

Some parrotfishes spend the nights under overhanging ledges of rock or in caves. When alarmed during the day they swim straight for their night quarters, in a direct line. Tests were made to see how they homed so accurately. First a net was hung in front of a cave and when the fishes were disturbed they swam straight for the net and continued trying to swim through it. When it was lifted they swam straight into the cave. The next test was to net some of the parrotfishes that were known always to swim in a south-easterly direction to their caves. They were then taken farther along the coast and put back into the sea. They immediately swam on a south-easterly course, to where there were no caves. When this experiment was repeated it was noticed that if a cloud passed across the sun the fish were temporarily lost. They swam about in different directions until the sun shone again, when they once more swam unerringly on a south-easterly course. Finally, the experiment was tried of blindfolding the fishes, by putting suction caps over their

1671

*Properly dressed for the night, a sleeping parrotfish **Scarus guacamaia**. At night certain parrotfish reveal a remarkable phenomenon—they secrete a loose mucous envelope around themselves. This envelope may take half an hour to secrete and the same time to break out of at daylight.*

eyes. They swam in all directions, quite confused, but when the caps were removed they swam straight for their caves.

Eating hard tack

With their parrot-beak teeth they browse the eelgrass and seaweeds, often nipping pieces off the coral. In this way they erode the coral reefs. The pieces of coral swallowed are ground by flattened teeth in the throat. The undigested coral fragments are passed out and dropped in special places along the route the parrotfishes follow to and from their caves, accumulating in heaps. The sound they make when crunching the coral can be heard by anyone standing nearby.

Several kinds of courtship

It is not easy to generalize about the behaviour of parrotfish as they differ so much from one species to another. It is the same with their breeding habits. The eggs of *Scarus* species are elongated and oval, those of *Sparisoma* are spherical. In the one species *Sparisoma rubripinna* in which the spawning habits have been closely studied it was found that it bred all the year round but only in the afternoons. Then, a milling mass of fishes leaves its feeding ground close inshore

and assembles in depths of 65—70 ft, the mass keeping a few feet up from the bottom. Most of the fishes assembled there are males, so while the spawning is going on there is a preponderance of females inshore. Every now and then groups of 4—13 swim upwards from the main mass and circle rapidly around to release eggs and milt. There is, however, a second type of spawning in which a solitary male mates with a solitary female. The bulk of the eggs come from the group spawning, however. In another species a male and a female swim up to the surface, circling round each other as they go. As they get near the surface they are rotating round each other, and then they release a cloud of eggs and milt. The eggs of all species contain an oil drop, so they float near the surface. They range from $\frac{1}{25} - \frac{1}{10}$ in. diameter, and they hatch in a day, to release the usual fish larvae.

Nightdress or pyjamas?

When some parrotfishes *Scarus guacamaia* were kept in aquaria in 1954 they were seen as night fell to give out mucus, or slime, from glands in their skin. Later, other parrotfishes were seen to do the same thing.

The mucus formed a kind of loose shroud with an opening in the front guarded by a flap that allowed water in and a hole at the back which let it out. So the parrotfish can draw water in and pass it across its gills to breathe even while enclosed in what is almost a plastic cover. In the morning the parrotfish breaks out of its 'nightdress' and goes about its normal activities. When a parrotfish rests at night its breathing drops to a low rate. It is to all intents sleeping. The mucus envelope may be a way of preventing the gills silting up while the fish is resting on a sandy bottom, or it may be a protection from enemies. It is not known whether all parrotfishes do this, or even whether those species that have been seen to do it always do so. Whatever the situation is, a fish that wraps itself up for the night like this must be unique.

class	**Pisces**
order	**Perciformes**
family	**Scaridae**
genera	***Scarus***
	Sparisoma
	others

Peccary

Peccaries are the South American equivalent of the Old World wild pigs, which superficially they resemble. They are smaller than the true pigs, however, and differ in other important details so they are placed in a separate family, the Tayassuidae.

Peccaries have long slim legs and small hooves and there are only three toes on the hindfeet, not four as in true pigs. The tail is vestigial and the body is covered with thick bristly hairs, which form a slight mane on the neck. When the peccary is agitated the hairs on the spine are raised, exposing a scent gland on the lower back. This gives out an unpleasant musky odour detectable at some distance. Peccaries have more complex stomachs and fewer teeth than true pigs, and their short sharp upper tusks grow downwards instead of upwards.

There are two species: the collared peccary which is found in deserts, woodland and rain forests from the southern borders of the United States to Argentina; and the white-lipped peccary, ranging from Paraguay to Mexico, which is less well-known as it lives deep in the tropical rain forests that cover much of this area.

The collared peccary is the smaller, standing 20 in. at the shoulder with a maximum length of about 37 in. and it weighs up to 65 lb. The coarse hair is black mixed with white, so the effect is greyish, and it owes its name to the narrow semi-circular collar of lighter hair on the shoulders. Alternative names are musk hog or javelina—the Spanish **javeline** means spear—descriptive of its spear-like tusks.

The white-lipped peccary is dark reddish brown to black in colour with, as the name suggests, an area of white round the mouth. It can be as much as 41 in. long and stands 24 in. at the shoulder.

John Tashjian at Tuxtla Gutierrer Zoo

A white-lipped peccary follows its nose. Peccaries have an extremely keen sense of smell and can even locate food an inch or so under the ground. Their senses of sight and hearing, on the other hand, are relatively weak. Peccaries have coarse, bristly hair, long slim legs and small hooves.

Safety in numbers

The speed and agility of peccaries, who move with a fast running gait when pursued, combined with a group defence system, protect them from dogs, coyotes and even bobcats. Although not normally aggressive to humans, an entire herd may counter-attack if one member of it is wounded or chased. They are hunted for their hides and meat, and when brought to bay the herds are described as standing in close formation, champing their tusks and making determined charges at their hunters.

Both species are gregarious, but whereas the collared peccary associates in groups of 5–15, the herds of the white-lipped peccary are much larger, being up to 100 or more. Males and females of all ages are found in these groups, which do not appear to move over large areas: the territorial range of the collared peccary for example is usually only about 3 miles.

The herds have no apparent leader and it has been suggested that the musk gland plays an important part in co-ordinating group movements. Peccaries of the same herd practise mutual grooming, in the course of which they rub their throats and shoulders on each other's musk glands, a habit known as 'smell-sharing behaviour'. In the normal course of events, secretions from these glands will also be transferred to low branches or bushes along paths frequented by the herds, thus making the home territory as well as fellow-members of a herd instantly recognisable by smell to each individual.

Grub up!

Peccaries are most active in the cooler hours of the day, and at night. Their usual resting place is in a thicket or under a large boulder, or they will readily take to the abandoned burrows of other animals. Their eyesight is not good and their hearing only fair but they have a keen sense of smell, being able for instance to locate an edible bulb an inch or so under the ground. The collared peccary is mainly vegetarian and uses its pig-like snout to root for fruit, berries and bulbs. It will, however, also eat grubs, occasionally small vertebrates and even

Peccary

White-lipped *(Tayassu pecari)*

Collared *(T. tajacu)*

1683

snakes; it appears to be immune to rattle-snake venom. The white-lipped peccary is more omnivorous, living on carrion, worms and insects as well as on a variety of fruits and roots, and is reputed to hunt larger prey. It is never far from running water.

Short infancy

Very little is known of the breeding habits of the white-lipped peccary, but in the collared species the litter consists of 1–4, normally 2, young, and many females breed twice in the same year. Gestation is variously given as 112–116 and 142–148 days. The young are born in a burrow, hollow log or cave. Their colour is quite different from an adult's, being reddish with a dark stripe down the back. They are able to run when a few hours old and are weaned at 6–8 weeks. Life expectancy is up to 20 years.

You scratch my back . . .

Peccaries like pigs are not 'dirty' animals; on the contrary they are quite clean, and have the habit of pawing sand against them-selves which is probably a cleaning action. Although the adults are unpredictable, pec-caries have been tamed. One kept as a pet in the United States National Zoological Park in Washington, DC, knew its name and would come when called or when it recog-nised a friend. Apparently it enjoyed having its back scratched with a stick as much as any domestic pig.

class	**Mammalia**
order	**Artiodactyla**
family	**Tayassuidae**
genus & species	***Tayassu pecari*** *white-lipped peccary* ***T. tajacu*** *collared peccary*

△ *Collared peccary yawns—and shows its tusks.* ▽ *Eating at home: family of collared peccaries.*

H Klingel

△ *Uropygid 'scorpion'* **Thelyphorus caudatus.** ▽ *Amblypygid pedipalp* **Damon variegatus.**

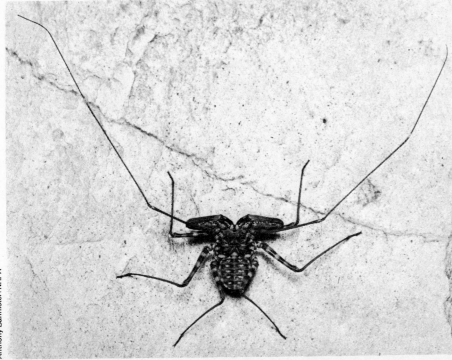

Anthony Bannister: NHPA

Pedipalpi

The pedipalpi are an artificial assemblage of animals, now regarded as belonging to three separate orders within the Arachnida. The members of two of these groups are both known as 'whip scorpions' but for different reasons: The 'whip' in one group, the Uropygi, is a long thin tactile tail at the end of the abdomen, while the other whip scorpions, the Amblypygi, carry two 'whips' in the form of a pair of very long, flexible legs. All three groups use the first pair of legs as feelers rather than for walking, but in the Amblypygi the length is particularly exaggerated. The members of the third group, the Schizomida, are too small and retiring to be well known. In all three, the body is in two parts, a combined head and thorax, or cephalothorax, and an abdomen of 12 segments. They vary in length from $1-2\frac{3}{4}$ in. The cephalothorax bears the legs and, at the front, a short pair of appendages called chelicerae followed by the well-developed pair which names the group pedipalps.

1685

Anthony Bannister: NHPA

△ *At death's door? This whip scorpion **Damon variegatus** traps and kills insects with its large spiny pedipalps and then dismembers them with its sharp, curved chelicerae. Two pairs of tiny eyes can be seen on top of the cephalothorax.*

Frog-eating tail-rumps ...

The powerful pedipalps of the Uropygi scorpion-like animals are armed with claws for the capture of cockroaches, grasshoppers and other insects, as well as slugs and worms—or even small frogs and toads in the case of the largest species *Mastigoproctus giganteus,* of Mexico and the southern United States. At the base of each pedipalp is a large semicircular toothed structure used for crushing the prey. There are 8–12 feeble eyes arranged in 3 groups on the cephalothorax, but the first pair of legs are more important as sense organs. In any case, the Uropygi are nocturnal hunters, hiding during the day under logs and stones, or in burrows. *M. giganteus* spends several days digging its burrow with its pedipalps and when it is finished the tunnel may be 4 in.

long. The prey is usually devoured here.

There are about 700 species of Uropygi (literally tail-rumps) living in southern North America and northeastern South America as well as in India, Malaya, eastern Asia and Japan.

... split middles ...

The members of the small group, the Schizomida, are $\frac{1}{4}$ in. or less long with at most only a knob for a tail. The carapace of the cephalothorax, divided in this order alone into three parts, carries only one pair of eyes. The pedipalps end in spines instead of in claws and they move up and down instead of sideways as in the Uropygi. There are three genera and the group occurs sporadically in tropical regions, appearing sometimes also in botanical gardens such as that at Kew. The Schizomida feed at night, probably on insects and hide by day, though not in any fixed home. When disturbed, they make their escape by a quick backwards leap and can run fast. Little more is known of their habits.

... and blunt-rumps

The tail-less Amblypygi, (literally bluntrumps) have very flattened bodies suitable for getting through narrow cracks and the two halves are joined by a slender stalk. There is one pair of median eyes and three pairs of lateral eyes as in some of the Uropygi. The pedipalps are spined, powerful and sometimes very long, and each ends in a movable hook. There are fewer than 100 species, $\frac{1}{4}$–$1\frac{3}{4}$ in. long, and they are found in humid tropical and subtropical regions: the southern half of Africa, America, India, Borneo and New Guinea.

Nocturnal like the others, the Amblypygi cling by day to the undersurfaces of rock crevices, logs and stones. Some species, with less need for dampness, have become commensal with man and in some parts of the world few houses are without them. When exposed to light, their first reaction is to freeze, but they will run fast if touched. Usually they walk sideways and then, as well as while at rest, they are continually searching around with the tips of their long

legs. One of the two families consists mostly of small cave-dwellers and these, unlike the others, can run around under the ceilings of caves or even up polished glass. The prey, mostly insects of various kinds, are held in the spiny pedipalps while the chelicerae remove pieces for chewing.

Courtship dances

Courtship and breeding have not been observed in many of the pedipalpi, but at least it is clear that the groups differ. In the Uropygi the courting male holds the long front legs of the female in his pedipalps and chelicerae and walks backwards with his mate following. She responds by lifting her abdomen which the male strokes with his front legs. The sperm is transferred in a spermatophore which is held against the female genital opening for some hours. The pregnant female digs a burrow where she stays several weeks and lays, in one species at least, 20–35 yellowish eggs which are retained in a transparent membrane under her abdomen. The young cut their way out

of this by means of special spines on their legs and cling to the upper side of the mother's abdomen or to the bases of her back legs until they reach the adult form, at the first moult. They then leave the mother whose strength is nearly spent and become adult after three more yearly moults.

In the single member of the Schizomida studied, the mating pair promenade with the female holding the end of the male's abdomen with her chelicerae. He then deposits a spermatophore and cements it to the ground. From the top of this, the female gathers the sperm. Later she builds a little nest with cemented walls under the soil. The Amblypygi court at night, with much tapping of the front legs and threatening with the pedipalps, but no grasping. The male deposits a slender transparent spermatophore on the ground while facing away from the female and then turns towards her and loads it with sperm. As he steps back and quivers, she collects the sperm, leaving the spermatophore for him to eat. She also carries her eggs in a sac under her abdomen.

Exaggerated reputation

With the scorpion-like tails of one group and the exaggerated legginess of the other, whip scorpions are unfailing objects of horror. In fact, they have neither stings nor venomous bites and the Amblypygi, at least, are harmless. Nevertheless, the large *Mastigoproctus giganteus* of southern North America, where it has the local name of 'grampus', is generally feared for its supposed venomous properties. In fact it can inflict a wound with the spines on its pedipalps and, like others of the Uropygi, can discharge a protective cloud into the air from glands near the base of the tail which can be very irritating to the mucous membranes. The secretion of some species smells of formic acid or chlorine, but in *M. giganteus* — called 'vinegarone' or 'vinegaroon' in America — it is acetic acid.

| phylum | **Arthropoda** |
| class | **Arachnida** |

Pelican

The pelican is known to many people only from seeing it in zoos or on ornamental lakes where its ungainly appearance often makes it the subject of ridicule. In the wild, however, it is a superb flier and swimmer.

There are eight species, two of which occur in the New World and six in the Old, distributed over the tropical and warm temperate parts of the globe. The species differ only in the smaller details of size, colour and geographical range. Both sexes are alike and all have massive bodies, supported on short legs with strong webbed feet. They have long necks, small heads and a thick, harsh plumage. They are among the largest living birds, from 50—72 in. long. The most conspicuous feature is the enormous beak; the upper part is flattened and the lower part carries a pouch that can be distended to grotesque proportions. It can hold about 17 pints of water and is used, not for storing food, but as a dip net for catching fish.

Apart from the brown pelican, in the majority of the species the adult plumage is mainly white, tinged with pink in the breeding season in some species such as the pink-backed pelican of Africa. The primaries are black or dark. Some species have crests and in some there is yellow, orange or red on the bill, pouch and bare part of the face. The brown pelican, the smallest member of the family, with a wing-span of up to 6½ ft and weighing about 8 lb, has a white head with a yellow tinge. In the breeding season the neck turns a rich brown with a white stripe running down each side. The wings and underparts are dark brown. The larger white species may have a wing-span of 10 ft and weigh 24 lb.

The brown pelican, which is a sea bird that does not venture far from the shore and breeds on small islands, is found along the south Atlantic and Gulf coasts of North America through the West Indies to Venezuela. Along the Pacific it ranges from central California to Chile with one population on the Galapagos Islands. The other New World species is the American white pelican that breeds on inland lakes from western Canada to southern Texas. In the Old World there are pelicans in Africa, southern Asia, including the Philippines, and Australia and in southeast Europe there are isolated colonies of the large silvery white Dalmatian pelican which ranges eastward from there into central Asia, visiting Egypt and northern India in winter. It nested at least as far north as Hungary until the middle of the last century and according to Pliny it nests in the estuaries of the Elbe, Rhine and Scheldt.

▷ Crowning glory! Pelicans often found their colonies in tall trees. The nests, unlined structures of dry twigs, are large and ungainly.
◁ Pink-backed pelican in flight.

Ram Panjabi

Fishing cooperation

Pelicans feed mainly on fish but crustaceans are also taken. The white pelicans fish while floating on the surface or wading about in the shallows. They thrust their heads under the water, using their pouches as dip nets to catch the fish. Occasionally a large flock of birds will cooperate by forming a line across the water and swimming abreast, beating the surface violently with their wings to drive schools of small fish into shallow water where they can easily scoop them up.

Community breeding

Pelicans are very sociable and all the species nest in large colonies sometimes of tens of thousands. Most of the white species breed on isolated islands in large inland lakes usually making their nests on the ground but occasionally they nest in low trees. On the ground the nest is sometimes just a depression scooped out of the earth. The brown pelican which breeds on small islands on the coast, makes a loose nest of sticks in mangrove trees and low shrubs or sometimes on the ground.

In all species the breeding season varies from place to place and from year to year. In some tropical areas they may even breed throughout the year. Chalky white eggs numbering 1—4 are laid which both parents help to incubate for 29—30 days. The babies are born naked and blind but quickly grow a soft white down. Both parents feed the young, at first dribbling regurgitated food out of the ends of their beaks into the chicks' open mouths, but after a few days the chicks are strong enough to stick their heads into their parents' pouches to get the food. Be-

◁ *Spectacular dive—spear-like attack.*
▽ *Head-on collision—clumsy recovery.*
The brown pelican feeds on fish which it sights from the air and then dives onto, rather like a gannet, striking the water with such force that fish as much as 6 ft below the surface may be stunned. The noise of the impact can sometimes be heard ½ mile away. Under the skin of its breast the brown pelican has a layer of air pockets enclosed in membranes which protects it when it hits the water.

fore the chicks are 2 weeks old they leave the nest and form noisy juvenile groups but the parents continue to feed them for some time. The young mature slowly, only acquiring adult plumage after several years. They seldom breed until they are 4 years old. Pelicans are long lived birds. Although the accepted record is 52 years, there are less well authenticated accounts of birds living to a much greater age. The Emperor Maximilian is said to have had a pelican which always accompanied his troops when they were on the march, and that lived for more than 80 years.

Many hazards for the young

Mature pelicans have few natural enemies. Sometimes they may be killed by sea lions in the Pacific or occasionally eaten by sharks but among the young mortality is very high. When the young birds congregate after leaving the nest many fall from trees or get caught in the branches or even trampled on by clumsy adults. When a baby pelican is hurt a larger fledgling is likely to eat it. The adult birds do little to protect their young and sometimes entire nesting colonies are wiped out by predatory animals. It is doubtful if even half the young birds survive. Fishermen have been known to destroy colonies of pelicans to prevent them taking so much fish. At Pelican Island, Florida, in 1911 a plague of mosquitoes caused an entire colony of breeding birds to abandon the rookery, leaving 600 nests containing nestlings. In Peru the guano diggers often damage the nests, knocking young birds out of the way and frightening away the parents, so leaving the chicks an easy prey for predators. Nowadays the pelican colonies are often in danger when marshes are drained or lakes dry up due to large water schemes.

Superb in flight

The pelican has often been described as a clumsy bird, a statement no more justified than it would be to speak of a duck or a swan as clumsy merely because they walk on

▷ *Helping itself. A pelican chick sticks its head into its parent's pouch to get its food.*

James Carr

Series by Jugo H Schroeder

land with a waddle and because the body is heavily built. When a pelican has managed after much effort and flapping to become airborne it is a strong and graceful flier, and it is no less graceful in the water. With legs up, head well back on the shoulders and its large bill resting on the front of the neck it can sail through the air with little effort.

Pelicans seem to possess quite unnecessary powers of flight considering that all their food is taken from the water and everything about them suggests adaptation to an aquatic mode of living. They fly at about 26 mph and there is an authentic record of their having maintained this speed for 8 miles, so it seems they also have the quality of endurance in flight. There is one record of the common pelican having achieved 51 mph. They regularly fly in formation either in line astern or in V-formation, all members of the flight beating their wings in perfect unison. The sight of a flock gliding down like a squadron of flying-boats is spectacular. They also have the vulture's trick of using thermal currents, soaring in spirals to

a great height, even as much as 8 000 ft, where by alternately flapping and gliding they may circle for hours.

Symbol of piety

The principal myth concerning the pelican is that the parent bird, if unable to find food for her brood, pierced her breast with the tip of her bill and fed the youngsters on her own blood, and that is how the bird is figured in the earliest pictures of it. It was because of this belief that the pelican was chosen as an emblem of charity and piety and became a favourite heraldic emblazonment. There is a different version of the story according to Bartholomew. Writing in 1535 he says that the young pelicans smite the parents in the face, whereupon the mother retaliates, hitting them back and killing them. Then, on the third day, the mother smites herself in the side until the blood runs out onto the bodies of her youngsters, bringing them to life again.

These two stories may have arisen because

△ *Fish scoop. A yawning common white pelican shows its enormous pouch for catching fish.*

in feeding its young the parent presses its bill against its neck and breast in order to make the contents of the pouch more readily available to the young, who thrust their bills into the pouch to take the food. The red tip on the common pelican's mandible may also have made the story more plausible.

class	**Aves**
order	**Pelecaniformes**
family	**Pelecanidae**
genus & species	***Pelecanus crispus*** Dalmatian *pelican* ***P. erythrorhynchos*** *American white pelican* ***P. occidentalis*** *brown pelican* ***P. onocrotalus*** *common white pelican* ***P. rufescens*** *pink-backed pelican others*

Peppered moth

The study of the peppered moth has provided us with an example of evolution in progress, the gradual change in form as a result of natural selection. There are three colour forms of the peppered moth. The typical form has white wings 'peppered' with black specks which sometimes form faint black lines. Another form called **carbonaria** *is the black or melanic form, from the black pigment called melanin. The third, an intermediate form, which is black, speckled with white, is called* **insularia**. *The females are larger, with a wingspan of about $2\frac{1}{4}$ in., the males having a wingspan of about $1\frac{3}{8}$ in. The males have feathery antennae while the females' are slender and hairlike.*

The peppered moth is found throughout Europe and may be identical with a North American moth that is classified as another species **Amphidasis cognateria**.

Darwin's missing evidence

Darwin's theory of evolution by natural selection lacked final proof: he could give no example of evolution actually taking place. Yet during his lifetime significant changes had taken place in the population of peppered moths in Britain and elsewhere. Before the Industrial Revolution the black or melanic form of the peppered moth, often called simply *carbonaria*, was extremely rare. It occurred as a rare mutant cropping up from time to time like red hair in man. Then, as towns and even countryside became coated with soot from homes and factories, melanic moths became more numerous and in some places the typical peppered moth completely disappeared. The soot not only blanketed the trees, but it also killed the lichens, so the typical form of peppered moth showed up starkly against the dark

▽ *Peppered moths. Typical and melanic forms on soot-covered tree (left) and on lichen (right).*

background of the trees on which it rests during the day and was easily picked off by insect-eating birds. The black variety which had been at a great disadvantage now flourished, because birds failed to see it on a soot-blackened tree. For many years now the peppered moth has been studied by HB Kettlewell and other biologists. They found that black, melanic, peppered moths now predominate in the industrial areas of Britain, and only in rural areas such as the southwest tip of England and the north of Scotland are they still very rare.

The phenomenon of the change from the typical to the black varieties in industrial areas is called industrial melanism and some 10% of the 700 or so larger moths in Britain have changed from a light pattern to dark shades. In all cases they are moths that spend the day resting against a tree trunk or similar background. It must not be thought, however, that a new species has been created, as light and dark peppered moths still interbreed. But it has been shown that an animal's form can change when its environment changes, because under the new conditions the new form is favoured at the expense of the old. Where smokeless zones have been introduced, the situation is being reversed with the typical, light variety once more becoming common.

Night fliers

The peppered moth belongs to the family Geometridae, or geometers as they are popularly known. These are night-flying moths that spend the day resting inconspicuously on tree trunks with the wings flat against the bark. The peppered moth can be found in May and June in woods and parks and its caterpillars feed on trees and bushes such as oak, elm, birch and bramble from July to September. The caterpillars of geometer moths are called 'loopers' because of the way they arch their bodies when walking. The name geometer means ground measurer which is very appropriate. To pupate they burrow into the soil and the adults emerge the following May.

The adults are extremely inconspicuous when they rest on tree trunks, although many are caught by bats when flying at night. The caterpillars are just as inconspicuous because they resemble twigs. They are green or brown with minute white dots and they rest with their head and body raised at an angle to a twig, hanging on with their hindlegs, or prolegs. Between the two pairs of prolegs are fleshy knobs which assist the camouflage by making it look as if the caterpillar is firmly attached to the twig, by eliminating any shadow under the body.

Proving the case

Since industrial melanism was first demonstrated, careful experiments have been made to show that the change in colour has been due to the effect of predators being able to find typical peppered moths more easily than black ones on a dark background. In other words, to prove that natural selection is taking place it must be shown that one form is better fitted to survive than another.

Dr Kettlewell watched birds catching peppered moths as they rested on trees. He marked large numbers of moths with paint and found that in an unpolluted forest he could recapture twice as many typical as black moths but that the proportion in a woodland close to an industrial city was reversed. This was clear evidence that moths that fitted their background lived longer. In another experiment, dead typical and dead black moths were placed on tree trunks in an industrial area. Birds found 60% more of the typical moths. Furthermore Kettlewell found that when moths were kept overnight in a cage painted with black and white stripes, black moths usually settled on black stripes and typical moths on white stripes, so apparently the moths are actively seeking the right background.

class	Insecta
order	Lepidoptera
family	Geometridae
genus & species	*Biston betularia*

Jane Burton: Photo Res

Perch

This fish, which originally gave its name to the largest order of fishes, the Perciformes, was the freshwater perch of Europe. The name is derived from Greek and Latin, through the French, and it was known to the Romans as **perca**. *There are many perch-like fishes known today, so the main attention here will be concentrated on the European perch. This plump-bodied fish is dark greenish with a yellowish tinge on the flanks and dark bars. The under-surface is silvery blue to yellowish, and the anal and pelvic fins are reddish. The colour varies, however, from one place to another, and in some localities the bars may be missing. The front dorsal fin is spiny, but both are well developed. There is a medium sized anal fin, the pelvic fins are well forward and the tail is almost square-ended. It usually weighs about 1 lb although the record is about 10 lb.*

The perch is found in freshwater in much of Europe, western Asia and Siberia, and in slightly brackish waters around the Baltic. Its counterpart in North America, east of the Rockies, is the yellow perch, which is golden with dark bars, a silver belly and orange anal and pelvic fins. A near relative in northern Europe, including the British Isles, is the pope or ruffe, a somewhat smaller fish with a marbled pattern and lines of distinct dark spots on the fins. The walleye or pikeperch of North America is about the same size as the perch but has a blotched pattern and prominent eyes. The pikeperch of Europe and Asia is about the same size as the walleye. In North America there are also small darters, fast-moving, brilliantly coloured fish, only a few inches long.

Lying in ambush

These well camouflaged predatory fish lurk among the stems of water plants, suddenly dashing out to seize their prey. The mouth is small but opens into a wide gape. Their main sense is sight but perch can hear and smell. There are two nostrils on each side of the head, one which takes water in and the other at the rear which lets water out of the nasal pouch. Inside this pouch is a rosette of sensitive tissue.

Perch live in shoals in slow-flowing rivers and lakes. The smaller the fishes, the larger the shoals, so at 3 years old they swim in small groups of a half-dozen or less, and later may even be solitary. In winter they retire to deeper water, as deep as 30 ft in lakes, and remain quiescent there. They can, if necessary, draw upon the oxygen in the swim bladder for breathing.

Fish food builds bonny perch

The adult perch eat smaller fishes, which they usually seize from behind with their sharp teeth, damaging the tail. They then swallow the fish head-first. The fry, up to one month old, feed on waterfleas and other small plankton, after which they eat bottom-living invertebrates, such as midge and mayfly larvae, freshwater shrimps and occasionally a leech. During July, when the small perch are about 2 months old, there is a tendency towards cannibalism. Perch feeding only on fish grow faster than those forced to eat other food when fish are scarce.

Strings of eggs

Spawning takes place during April and May, the fishes shoaling according to size. The eggs, like those of the American yellow perch, are laid in long strings which become entangled with water plants. In laying them the female glides over the water plants with her fins lowered, shedding the eggs which are then fertilised by one or more males. A large female may lay 200 000 eggs. They hatch in about 18 days, or in only 8 – 10 days if the weather is warm. The transparent larvae are $\frac{1}{5}$ in. long. On hatching, each larva spirals to the surface to fill its airbladder. After this they hang for a while on water plants, and then float at the surface. Perch mature at 3 years. The maximum recorded life span is 10½ years.

Do fish feel pain?

One of the questions often asked is whether fishes feel pain. The story usually told, to show they do not, is about the angler whose hook fouled the eye of a perch. In freeing the hook the eye was removed and the angler used it as bait, catching the perch it belonged to almost immediately. It is an unpleasant story, yet a point is made. Almost equally unpleasant reading is the fact that since 1825 a dozen or more scientists have tried the experiment of removing the forebrain of fishes, mainly of perch – probably because they were easy to get. The forebrain is the 'thinking' part of the brain. In these experiments it was found that the fishes soon recovered from the operation and, so far as one could see, led quite normal lives. Presumably, therefore, if they feel pain at all, it cannot be to anything like the same degree as human beings.

class	Pisces
order	Perciformes
family	Percidae
genera & species	*Acerina cernua* pope *Etheostoma nigrum* johnny darter *Perca fluviatilis* European perch *P. flavescens* yellow perch *Stizostedion vitreum* walleye others

◁ *A European perch lurks among the water plants waiting for unsuspecting prey. Its deceptively small mouth opens into a wide gape.*

△ *A rather drab relative, the walleye's most notable feature is its prominent eyes, the chief sense organ of perch.*

▷ *Design in eggs. Part of an egg rope of European perch wrapped around a water plant. Developing embryos can be seen inside the translucent eggs.*

John Tashjian

Heather Angel

Père David's deer

This deer has been extinct in the wild for many years and is now known only from the descendents of a herd kept in the Emperor's hunting park near Peking. It was discovered in 1865 by the French missionary and naturalist, Père Armand David. It is quite the strangest of the Asiatic deer; it looks like a donkey with long antlers. The front prong of the antlers is forked but the hind prong is usually straight and slender. Unlike those of other deer, the antlers are sometimes shed twice a year, the summer antlers, measuring 28–35 in. along the curve, being dropped in November and the second, much smaller pair, if they occur, are hard by January and dropped a few weeks later. The females have no antlers. Père David's deer stands about 45 in. at the shoulder and the coat is reddish tawny mixed with grey. The underparts and a ring round the eye are white. There is a mane on the neck and throat and the tail is tufted and longer than that of any other deer. The hoofs are large and spreading.

Original habitat unknown

Even the Chinese did not know where Père David's deer came from originally but it is thought it may have inhabited the swampy plains of northern China until cultivation of the land wiped it out except for some kept by the Emperors in their hunting parks. The species now survives only in herds in Woburn Park, England and various zoos throughout the world.

Unlike most deer it is very fond of water. It swims well and will spend long periods standing in water up to its shoulder. The late Duke of Bedford has recorded in his book *The Years of Transition* that he has seen young stags racing and playing in deep water more in the manner of seals than of deer. Although predominantly a grazing animal, in summer Père David's deer supplements its grass diet with waterplants.

Boxing stags

The rut begins in June when the hinds group together in harems dominated by a stag. The master stag often engages in mock combat and actual fights with rival stags for the possession of the harem. He will use not only his antlers and teeth when fighting but will also rise on his hind legs and box like the red deer. The master stag sires the early calves until driven out by another stag, and this goes on until the rut ends in August. The stags usually keep together, away from the hinds, for about 2 months before and 2 months after the rut, but the sexes are together for the rest of the year. The one or two boldly spotted fawns are born in April and May after a gestation period of 250 days. The life span of the deer is at least 20 years.

Missionary and naturalist

Père David's deer has a quite unusual history. In 1865 Père David looked over the wall of the Chinese Emperor's hunting park near Peking and saw a herd of about 100 strange-looking deer. The Chinese called it *ssu-pu-hsiang* ('the four unlikes') for it was credited with having the antlers of a stag, the neck of a camel, the hoofs of a cow and the tail of a donkey. The Chinese believed the antlers had medicinal properties and they also carved small works of art from them. No stranger, however, was allowed into the park and it was not until the following year that Père David managed, by bribing the Tartar guards, to obtain two skins to send back to Paris. Later, several live individuals were shipped across to Europe to various zoos.

In 1894 a disastrous flood in China breached the wall of the Imperial hunting park and most of the herd of Père David's deer escaped into the surrounding countryside where many were killed and eaten by the starving peasants. Most of the survivors were destroyed in 1900 during the Boxer Rebellion and by 1911 only two remained alive in China and 10 years later both these were dead.

The deer sent to the European zoos did not breed very successfully and in 1900 the 11th Duke of Bedford decided that the only hope of saving the species was to collect all the survivors in one herd in Woburn Park and the famous herd was accordingly started with 18 deer. The park seemed to suit the deer and the herd flourished so by 1939 it numbered about 250. Meanwhile the Duke had been succeeded by his son who decided that with the risk of bombing, food shortages and disease during the war the species might once again face extinction. It seemed far from sensible to keep all the living members of a species in one place. Accordingly he approached the Zoological Society of London in 1944 and with their help day-old calves from the herd at Woburn were sent to Whipsnade Zoo and in time a small herd was established there, and this has continued to increase. Calves from Woburn and Whipsnade were subsequently sent to zoos in almost every part of the world, but perhaps what is of most interest is that in 1956 the Zoological Society of London presented four calves to the Peking Zoo, half a century after the species had been wiped out in China. There are now over 400 of these deer at Woburn and in various zoos.

class	**Mammalia**
order	**Artiodactyla**
family	**Cervidae**
genus & species	***Elaphurus davidianus***

◁ *Père Armand David, who discovered these deer when he looked over the wall of the Chinese Emperor's hunting park in Peking.*
▽ *A mixed society. The male has a fine head of antlers in summer but usually sheds these in November, growing a smaller pair in winter.*
▷ *A stag spends much time wallowing and will use its antlers to hook mud and turves skilfully onto its back, presumably as a pre-rut dressing.*

Peregrine

The peregrine is one of the best known of the falcons and a favourite among falconers. It is a large bird, 15—19 in. long, the female being larger than the male. Its upperparts are slate-blue with darker barrings, its underparts white with black barring. Young peregrines are browner with streaked rather than barred underparts. There are prominent black 'moustachial' stripes on each side of the face. These probably absorb light, so reducing glare from the ground that would prevent the peregrine from seeing its prey clearly.

Peregrines are almost cosmopolitan, living on all continents except Antarctica, and on many oceanic islands. They differ quite considerably throughout their range both in size and colouring, and so are divided into several subspecies. The largest peregrines live in Arctic regions and the smallest in the deserts of North America and Arabia. Peregrines are found over most of Europe and much of Asia and Africa, including Madagascar. They also inhabit most of North America, including the far north, but are absent from the southern parts of the United States and most of Central and South America, except at the southern tip of the continent. Finally they are found in Australia, and the islands to the north.

Alarming decrease

Although found in forests, open plains and moors, peregrines are most numerous in rocky areas of mountains and, in particular, sea cliffs. Each pair defends a territory, the size of which depends on the abundance of food. On cliffs where seabirds nest there may be a pair of peregrines every two miles but elsewhere territories may cover tens of square miles. When not feeding or caring for young, peregrines roost on a favourite perch or circle around their territory. Peregrines breeding in high latitudes migrate in winter, European birds crossing the equator to South Africa, for instance. They follow well-defined routes, usually hugging the coast but sometimes crossing open water. Occasionally the young birds travel with their parents.

In common with many other birds of prey, peregrines are becoming rare. Their decline started with the spread of intensive agriculture and game preserves. During the first half of this century, however, in Britain at least, the peregrine was recovering its numbers, with only a setback in the Second World War when they were killed to protect carrier pigeons being used as messengers. But since about 1955 there has been an alarming decline of peregrines in many parts of the world. This is due to pesticides which become concentrated in the eggs of birds of prey and make them infertile. Seeds treated with tiny amounts of insecticides are eaten by small mammals and birds. As they eat many seeds, larger amounts of insecticides are accumulated. The peregrine eats many small mammals and birds, so concen-

△△ *Blind magnificence: powerful peregrine.*
△ *Falconry was a serious sport in former times, the birds being used to catch game.*

E & M Baumann

trating the insecticide further. The dose they receive is seldom enough to kill them but when it gets into the eggs it will kill the embryo. In Britain today the population of peregrines is less than half what it was during the immediate postwar years.

Stooping to conquer

Peregrines feed mainly on birds but also on mammals such as young hares, mice and voles and occasionally amphibians and insects. Pigeons are favourite prey, although smaller races take more small birds. Grouse are often caught on moors and seabirds around cliffs. Prey is caught after a swift dive, or stoop, with nearly closed wings and is either killed in the air by being struck with the hind claws or is carried to the ground, and thence to a special feeding place where it is plucked before being eaten. They also sweep birds from their perches but the prey sometimes succeeds in escaping by violent manoeuvres or by hugging the ground. Yet peregrines will also take birds from the ground, as shown by their thefts of poultry. In the Arabian deserts peregrines are flown at bustards which land and fight on the ground. Peregrines are also used to keep other birds away from airfields.

Aerial exchanges

Peregrines mate for life and use the same nest site year after year. Sometimes the nest is a scrape in the ground and at other times the abandoned nest of a raven, herring gull

or buzzard is used. The most popular nest sites are on cliffs and are often inaccessible except to expert climbers. Occasionally peregrines nest on buildings and one pair even used a nestbox put out for it.

At the start of the breeding season the male perches near the nest site and when a female appears he flies out and back, calling to attract her. During courtship the pair dive and swoop or the two tumble through the air together, screaming frequently.

There are usually 3 or 4 eggs in each clutch, although there may be as many as 6. They are laid at 2—3 day intervals and incubation starts before all the eggs are laid so they hatch at intervals after a period of about one month. The female does most of the incubation and is fed by the male who brings food to her on the nest or passes it to her in the air or on a feeding perch. The female is very aggressive, attacking other large birds, men and dogs that come near the nest. When the chicks first hatch the female broods them, then after a fortnight she only covers at night. The male continues to bring food to the female who, in turn, feeds the chicks starting with the oldest. When the chicks are older the male may give food to them directly. These leave the nest when 5—6 weeks old and remain dependent on their parents for another 2 months, sometimes migrating with them.

Incredible speed

Although probably not held in such esteem as the gyrfalcon, the peregrine was a royal bird in mediaeval falconry. Even in strong winds it flies under perfect control and is capable of breathtaking accuracy when stooping, so it is not surprising that it was extremely popular, especially as it is easily tamed. Peregrines can be flown at birds as big as bustards or herons. Arab peregrines may kill seven or eight bustards in a day.

Various attempts have been made at estimating the speed of a peregrine's stoop and recent estimates show that it may be well in excess of 250 mph. This is an incredible speed and poses more problems than merely that of supplying power and streamlining to achieve such a speed. The bones, sinews and muscles must be strong enough to stand the strains imposed, especially during manoeuvring and braking, while the senses must be extremely acute and the reactions quick. One problem that the peregrine has neatly solved is that of breathing air that is rushing past at 200 mph or more. Its nostrils are ridged and within each nostril is a rod with two fins behind it. As air rushes past the nostril the flow is broken up as it swirls past the rod and fins, so little effort is needed to suck it in. Other fast-flying birds of prey have similar structures, but slower species such as vultures and sea eagles lack them.

class	**Aves**
order	**Falconiformes**
family	**Falconidae**
genus & species	***Falco peregrinus***

▷ *The deadly accuracy of a peregrine triumphs again as it towers over a victim, a duck.*

Peripatus

Peripatus is one of the most extraordinary animals living today. A relict from the past, it is a link between the soft-bodied ringed worms, such as the earthworm, and the hard-bodied arthropods, which include insects, spiders and crustaceans.

Its body is rather worm-like, tapering towards the hind end. It is 1–3 in. long but can be extended or contracted, and is sinuous in movement. The colour of peripatus is very variable, ranging from dark slate to reddish-brown in the various species, and there is usually a dark stripe down the back. The skin is dry and velvety to the touch and there are 20 or so pairs of short baggy legs each ending in a pair of hooks and ringed like the body. There is a pair of flexible antennae on the head with an eye at the base of each. The eyes are simple although each has a lens. They are directed outwards and upwards and probably do no more than distinguish between light and darkness. The sensory hairs clothing the antennae and most of the body are organs of touch and taste.

Must live in damp places

Peripatus is dependent on moist conditions, being found only in damp forests in South Africa, Australasia and South America. It lives under stones, rotting wood, the bark of fallen trees and similar damp places, being unable to withstand drying. In a dry atmosphere it will lose a third of its weight in less than 4 hours and will dry up twice as fast as an earthworm, and 40 times as fast as a smooth-skinned caterpillar its own size. The cause lies in its breathing system. An insect breathes through branching tubes or tracheae. Because the openings are few there is little loss of water and, moreover, there is an efficient mechanism for closing the openings when necessary. Peripatus has unbranched breathing tubes so it needs far more of them, with an opening to each tube, which means a rapid loss of water from the body when the surroundings are dry. As a result peripatus is found in 'islands', damp localities separated from other colonies by dry country.

Sticky threads for defence

The moment peripatus is disturbed it throws out one or two jets of a milky-white fluid from little nozzles or oral papillae, on the head, one either side of the mouth. On contact with the air the fluid solidifies immediately into sticky beaded threads of slime 3–12 in. long. The fluid is in reservoirs, one each side of the head, shaped like the rubber teat of an eye-dropper. Although the threads stick to one's fingers they do not stick to the velvety skin of peripatus itself, but insects and other small animals become entangled in them.

This entangling seems to be accidental because the threads serve more as a defence. Their food is mainly small insects such as termites and they also eat other small animals such as woodlice.

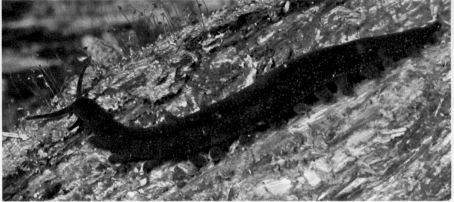

Going for a stroll: a peripatus from New Zealand **Peripatoides novaezealandiae.**

MF Soper

Casual love-making

The mating of peripatus can only be described as casual. The male places capsules containing sperms on the female, apparently at random since he will place them even on her legs. He may place them at times on another male. For a long time it was not known how the sperms reached the ova. Then it was found that white blood corpuscles in the female body migrate to the skin immediately beneath a capsule and break through it by digesting the cells of the skin. At the same time the lower wall of the capsule breaks and the sperms enter the female's blood stream and find their way to an ovary. There in large numbers they force their way through the wall of the ovary. If an immature female receives sperms the young egg cells feed on them and grow for a year before they are ready to be fertilised by a second mating. Except in a few species which lay eggs the embryos develop in the uterus taking in nourishment from the mother through its walls. In one South American species special tissues are formed, making a kind of placenta, to pass food from the mother's body to the growing embryos. Development takes 13 months and as young are born each year there is one month in each year when a female is carrying two sets of embryos, one just beginning to develop, the other nearly ready to be born.

500 million year old fossil of **Xenusion** *(left) looks remarkably like peripatus living today. Diagram (right) of* **Xenusion** *structure.*

Natural History Museum

Evolutionary bridge

The theory of evolution, in which it is assumed life began in water, requires two main invasions of the land. One, by the vertebrates, meant a change from gill-breathing to lung-breathing and indications of how this may have taken place are seen in the lungfishes (p 1356), the coelacanth (p 481) and the various newts and salamanders. Among the fossils, also, there is an almost complete series showing how this came about. The other invasion is that which brought the invertebrates on land, and the most important change was that from the aquatic ringed worms (see fanworm p 738) and the crustaceans, leading to insects and spiders. If one were asked to draw a hypothetical animal to bridge the gap between the ringed worms and the insects, one could not fail to draw something very like peripatus. Moreover, in its internal structure as well as its outward appearance, this animal looks like the forerunner of both millipedes and centipedes, and they in turn look like forerunners of modern insects. We know from fossils that insects, millipedes and centipedes, in the form we know them today, were already in existence 400 million years ago, so any ancestors linking the two must have been in existence even earlier. It is of interest therefore to find there is a fossil *Xenusion* in the rocks of over 500 million years ago that looks almost the same as peripatus. It is little more than a rusty coloured stain in a piece of limestone rock, yet its shape and the structure of its body and legs can be seen clearly enough to leave little doubt that the peripatus living today and the *Xenusion* of 500 million or more years ago could be closely related. From it or from animals very like *Xenusion* began the line which, through numerous changes, led to the millipedes, centipedes and insects, while another line of descent was continued, almost unchanged, in peripatus. Perhaps the most remarkable thing of all is that peripatus, having become thoroughly land-living, and having acquired a dry skin, should have kept a breathing system tying it so completely to damp areas.

phylum	**Arthropoda**
class	**Onychophora**
genus	***Peripatus capensis***
& species	***P. moseleyi,*** *others*

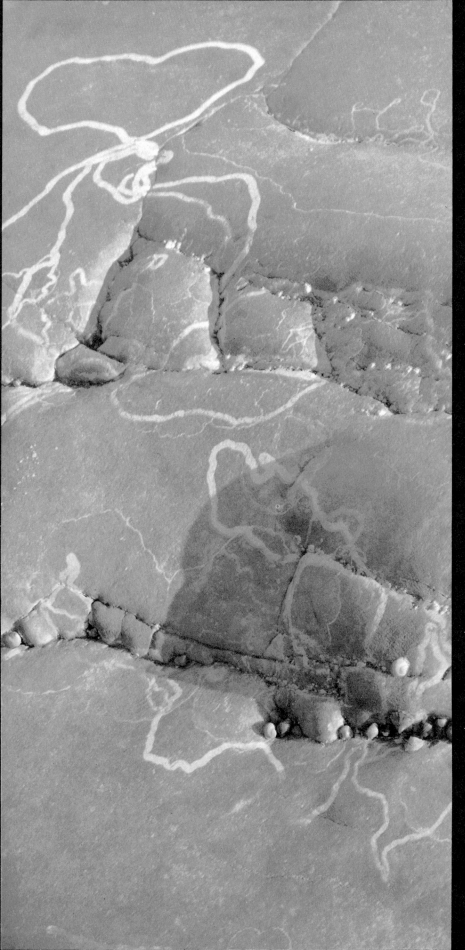

Periwinkle

Periwinkles are just one of the many types of sea snails. The original Anglo-Saxon name was pinewinclan or winewinclan and was applied to the largest of the European species of **Littorina**. Today periwinkle, or its shortened form winkle, is applied to several related species in other parts of the English-speaking world, notably North America. Zoo-logically four species of periwinkle are important; they show how the animals of the seashore are arrangea in zones, and probably represent marine species that are progressing towards life on land.

The original or common periwinkle is the largest. Its coiled shell is up to $1\frac{1}{2}$ in. high, and it is the one that, for a long time, has been collected in large quantities for food. Its shell, usually black, sometimes brown or red, is ridged in young, smooth in older individuals. The flat periwinkle with its rounded, flattened shell never reaches more than $\frac{1}{2}$ in. across. Its colour is variable, ranging from bright yellow or olive green, to brown, black or striped. The rough periwinkle has a ribbed shell, with a more pointed apex than the flat periwinkle, is yellow or white, and is $\frac{1}{2}$ in. across and $\frac{5}{8}$ in. high. The small periwinkle, dark reddish brown, is conical, about $\frac{1}{4}$ in. high.

The periwinkle shell has a round mouth which is closed by a dark horny disc, or operculum, permanently attached to the animal's foot. This is popularly called the 'winkle head'. The true head has a broad muzzle and two tapering tentacles with an eye at the base of each. The underside of the foot has a line down the middle and a periwinkle crawls by waves of contraction passing forward along the two halves of the foot alternately. Breathing is by a single feathery gill in the mantle cavity. All periwinkles are vegetarian and, as in other snails, rasp their food to pieces with a horny tongue, or radula.

The rough and common periwinkles are numerous throughout the North Atlantic. The small periwinkle ranges from Scandinavia to the Mediterranean and Black Sea, the flat periwinkle from Iceland to the Mediterranean.

Not knowing which way to turn: these slime tracks left behind on the rocks near high water mark show the aimless meanderings of rough periwinkles in their search for food. Now the tide is out the periwinkles are sheltering in damp rock crevices to avoid the heat of the sun.

A shore quartet

Four of the periwinkles, although closely related, survive in markedly different situations on the seashore where they may be covered by the tide once every 11–12 hours or exposed to parching sun and wind with no more than an occasional splash of salty spray for many days on end.

The small periwinkle lives in crevices in the rocks up in the splash zone, which is that part of the shore above extreme high tide that is wetted by spray only at the time of high spring tides. It may be completely immersed in water when, especially in winter, storms drive the tides higher than normal. It feeds on lichens, so it is more a land than an aquatic animal, and can survive without water for about 30 days.

The rough periwinkle lives between mid-tide level and the base of the splash zone, uncovered for long periods twice a day. It is, in fact, less tolerant of life in water than exposed to the air, and marked individuals have been found to have survived out of water for long periods. It feeds on seaweeds.

The flat periwinkle lives farther down the shore than the first two, among the larger wracks, on which it feeds, and under which it shelters to keep damp. It also feeds on sponges, especially the purse sponge, but to what extent is not known.

The common periwinkle lives from the level of low water spring tides to high water neap tides, on bare rocks, among seaweeds and stones or on sandy shores. Its tracks over the sand are commonly seen when the tide is out. On hot days, at low tide, however, it tends to get in under seaweed or into damp crevices, or to glue itself to rock surfaces. It gives out a slime from the foot as it withdraws into its shell which glues the edge of the opening to the rock. At the same time it closes itself in with the operculum. Although tight enough to prevent it drying up, its hold on the rock is so loose that a slight gust of wind may blow it off. The common periwinkle feeds on seaweed and especially on fragments broken away that are beginning to decompose.

Different ways of breeding

The sexes are separate, females being slightly smaller than males. In all periwinkles there is a definite mating, with internal fertilisation. The small periwinkle spawns every fortnight from September to April, to coincide with the highest tides and the greatest amount of spray. The larvae spend a long time in the plankton and eventually settle far down the shore and then make their way up to the splash zone 'on foot'. In the rough periwinkle the young develop inside the female and are born as small replicas of the parents. Breeding takes place most of the year. The flat periwinkle lays its eggs in masses of jelly on seaweed, from March to October. There is no swimming larva, the young leaving the jelly as tiny snails. The common periwinkle spawns in spring, the larvae swimming about for 2–3 months before settling on

△ *Cautious movement by a flat periwinkle.*
△▷ *Common periwinkles cluster on a rock.*
△▷▷ *Flat periwinkles on knotted-wrack.*

the shore as tiny winkles of less than pin-head size. The eggs are laid in capsules, 1–3 eggs in a capsule, which float, the larvae coming out of them after 6 days, to swim in the plankton. Each female may lay up to 5 000 eggs in a season.

Poor man's food

Many periwinkles are taken by shore birds, such as gulls and waders, while the tide is out. Oystercatchers, plovers, redshank and such waders feed on them, and when the tide is in bottom-feeding fishes such as plaice take them. They are, however, protected to a large extent from animals that swallow them whole by being able to shut themselves tight in their shells. One periwinkle, for example, was unharmed after being swallowed by a sea-anemone 24 days previously, and they can pass through sea-birds unharmed.

Man has been one of the main predators for centuries. In the 19th century, and in the early part of the 20th century at least, winkles were the 'poor man's food' in England and large quantities were eaten, cooked and extracted with a pin. How far this goes back is hard to say but in the caves in France and Italy, associated with mammoth bones of prehistoric times, necklaces have been found of winkle shells pierced and strung together.

DP Wilson

Heather Ange

▽ *Rocky shore zonation: there are 3 basic zones on rocky shores each distinguished by the animals and plants that live in them. This diagram shows the zonation of the four British species of periwinkle and of some seaweeds. The uppermost zone, the splash zone, is only wetted by a few tides a year, or by waves and splash. The small periwinkle lives here. The middle and largest part of the shore, the midlittoral zone, is subdivided into 3 belts. Each belt is inhabited by 1 or 2 species of periwinkle. This zone is exposed to air and covered by sea every day. The sublittoral zone is usually covered by sea. Few periwinkles live here.*

From sea to land

Animals and plants living on the shore tend to be arranged in zones, from high tide mark to low tide mark. In some the zonation tends to be obscured by local conditions, but one that is more clearly marked than most is the zoning of the periwinkles. Another aspect of this is that the arrangement of the four periwinkle species suggests that they are in process of becoming land animals; or, if not that, they suggest how a marine mollusc could become land-living. Three species feed on seaweed, one feeds on lichens. Two breathe by a gill in the mantle cavity which must be bathed with seawater. The other two, the small and the rough periwinkles, have very small gills and the mantle cavity acts as a lung. It only needs the young to develop inside the mother and be born as small but fully formed snails, with no larval period, for a life on land to be within reach, and this has already happened in the small periwinkle.

phylum	**Mollusca**
class	**Gastropoda**
order	**Mesogastropoda**
family	**Littorinidae**
genus & species	***Littorina littoralis*** *flat periwinkle* ***L. littorea*** *common periwinkle* ***L. neritoides*** *small periwinkle* ***L. saxatilis*** *rough periwinkle*

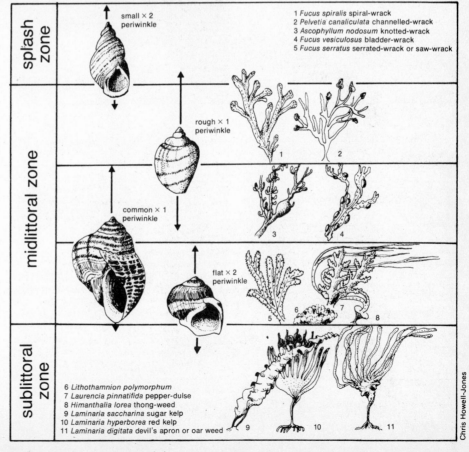

splash zone

midlittoral zone

sublittoral zone

small × 2 periwinkle

rough × 1 periwinkle

common × 1 periwinkle

flat × 2 periwinkle

1 *Fucus spiralis* spiral-wrack
2 *Pelvetia canaliculata* channelled-wrack
3 *Ascophyllum nodosum* knotted-wrack
4 *Fucus vesiculosus* bladder-wrack
5 *Fucus serratus* serrated-wrack or saw-wrack

6 *Lithothamnion polymorphum*
7 *Laurencia pinnatifida* pepper-dulse
8 *Himanthalia lorea* thong-weed
9 *Laminaria saccharina* sugar kelp
10 *Laminaria hyperborea* red kelp
11 *Laminaria digitata* devil's apron or oar weed

Chris Howell-Jones

1703

Phalanger

The phalangers make up the largest and most widespread family of Australian marsupials. There are some 46 species in the family Phalangeridae, which includes the cuscuses (p 596), the brushtail opossum (p 295) and the flying phalanger (p 800), as well as the koala (p 1251) which at one time was placed in a family on its own. The word phalanger is Greek and means a web, and it refers to the web of skin joining the small second and third toes. The claws on these two toes are divided and together they form a comb, used for grooming the fur. The name is not derived, as has sometimes been stated, from **phalanges** meaning toes and fingers.

The kangaroos and wallabies also have the second and third toes on the hindfeet small and joined by a web of skin, but they have only four toes on the hindfoot whereas phalangers have five toes on each foot. In the ringtailed opossums the first two fingers of the forefeet are opposable to the other three and can be used for gripping.

Squirrels outdone

With rare exceptions phalangers live in the tops of the trees, rarely coming to ground. The exceptions include a few, like the rock-haunting ringtailed opossum, and the scaly-tailed possum, which sleeps among rocks but which goes up into the trees at night to feed. Their life in the trees recalls the tree squirrels in other parts of the world, as does the way many of them move through the trees. They go from branch to branch, and from one tree to another, but in doing so they seem to glide rather than bound like the red and grey squirrels of the northern hemisphere. During the day they rest in nests made of leaves and twigs, in hollows in trees.

Phalangers as a group, however, show a greater diversity in shape than squirrels; some have bushy tails, and some have feather-like or pen tails, while others such as the brush-tipped ringtailed opossum have a slight suspicion of a flying membrane. At the other extreme, there are those like the flying phalanger which resemble the flying squirrels very closely. In Africa there are the so-called scaly-tailed flying squirrels. These are not true squirrels but are more nearly related to rats; they have bushy tails that are scaly on the underside near the base of the tail. This scaly part acts as a kind of climbing iron. The scaly-tailed possum has gone one better; its whole tail is scaly and the tip is prehensile.

Tapping for insects

We could go from one to the other of the phalangers and show how between them they seem to have used all the structures found in tree-dwelling animals elsewhere. But perhaps the most remarkable parallelism is seen in the striped possums. Most phalangers are wholly or nearly vegetarian, feeding on fruits and leaves but some also eat some insects. The striped possum, on the other hand, eats a few leaves and fruits but feeds

△ *A leaping ringtailed opossum . . .*

mainly on insects. It sniffs around and at the same time drums on the bark with its forefeet. Having located an insect grub it tears away the bark and rotten wood with its incisors. If it cannot then reach the grub with its teeth it hooks it out with its very long fourth finger. Except for a few minor details this could be a description of the feeding method of the aye-aye (p 113), a Madagascan lemur.

. . . and his cosy nest of bark strips and leaves.

Forward opening pouch

Female phalangers, except for the koala, have a pouch opening forwards with either 2 or 4 teats in it. Most of them carry one young at a time, rarely 2, but some of the smaller species may bear 5 or 6 young. The breeding and life-history generally seem to be much the same as in kangaroos and wallabies.

Dangers of infancy

Because they are nocturnal, and because they live so much in the tops of trees, most phalangers seem to have few enemies. The present danger to them is the felling of trees to clear the ground. Perhaps one of their main natural hazards is revealed in recent information about the social behaviour of the brushtail opossum. Each female has a territory of 2¾ acres, and each male has one of 7½ acres. Young males have difficulty in finding a vacant territory and are harried from pillar to post by the adults in occupation. Where this happens, there is a high infant mortality.

Playing possum

There is, and probably will always be, a confusion of names in this family, simply because Captain Cook thought the first phalanger he saw looked so like the North American opossum, as indeed it did. The name of the North American animal was shortened to possum, in about 1613, but zoologists continued to write 'opossum'. When Cook recorded seeing his first Australian animal he wrote 'possum' in his diary, so Australians, the older zoologists among them, continue to call it possum. Although some of the newer generation of Australian zoologists try to use the word 'phalanger' they often, almost unconsciously, lapse into 'possum'.

Perhaps confusion in this matter is appropriate because there is another slight mix-up. The North American opossum is said to feign dead, or play possum, whenever it is alarmed. This has been regarded for a long time as a distinct difference between the two animals. Now we are told by some people who know the American opossum well that they have never seen one play possum. This merely means that they have not seen it, because it does happen, but their experience suggests it is more rare than we used to suppose. Now, in his recent book, *A Continent in Danger*, Vincent Serventy tells of seeing an Australian possum playing possum—the first record we have of this.

class	**Mammalia**
order	**Marsupialia**
family	**Phalangeridae**
genera & species	***Dactylopsila trivirgata*** striped possum ***Distoechurus pennatus*** pentailed phalanger ***Hemibelideus lemuroides*** brush-tipped ringtailed opossum ***Petropseudes dahlii*** rock-haunting ringtailed opossum ***Pseudocheirus lanuginosus*** common ringtailed opossum ***Wyulda squamicaudata*** scaly-tailed possum, others

Phalarope

Phalaropes are small waders with needle shaped bills, and lobes on the toes, like those of coots but not so well developed. The roles of the sexes are reversed and the females are larger and more brightly coloured than the males. In the winter both sexes have drab plumage. The largest of the three species is Wilson's phalarope, about 10 in. long. In its breeding plumage the female is generally slate grey above and white beneath, with red-brown stripes on the back and on the throat. A broad black stripe runs through the eye and down the side of the neck. The male is mainly light brown above and white underneath. The grey phalarope is slightly smaller with a shorter bill. The female, in summer, has distinctive chestnut underparts, white patches over the eyes and a yellow bill. The male is less colourful and in winter both sexes are grey above and white underneath. The grey phalarope is a name used in the British Isles and aptly describes the plumage of those birds that come across the Atlantic in winter. In North America they are called red phalaropes which is appropriate for the birds in their breeding plumage. There are also alternative names for the third species: it is known as the red-necked phalarope in Britain and the northern phalarope in America. It is the smallest phalarope, about 6½ in. long, and has a very fine bill. In the winter it closely resembles the grey phalarope but in summer it is distinguishable by a black bill, slate grey head and upperparts, white throat and underparts and orange patches on the neck.

Phalaropes breed in northern parts of the world, migrating south in winter. The red phalarope breeds farther north than the others, around northern coasts of Alaska, Canada and Asia, as far as Spitzbergen. The distribution of the northern phalarope is similar but more to the south. Wilson's phalarope breeds inland in the central United States and Canada.

▽ Dabbling grey phalaropes resplendent in summer plumage. It is the female, on the right, who 'wears the trousers' for she is the most brightly coloured and aggressive of the pair and establishes the breeding territory.

Arthur Christiansen

Deep-sea waders

Although classified as waders, phalaropes do not wade in shallow water but swim, floating very high in the water because air is trapped in their very dense plumage. Wilson's phalarope is an inland bird and sometimes feeds on land but the other two nest near the coast, usually close to ponds or lakes and are virtually seabirds outside the breeding season. They sleep afloat and rarely come to land during the winter. Because they are very light, however, they get blown by gales; they are swept across the Atlantic, for instance, and driven inland to be recorded eagerly by keen birdwatchers.

Stirring for food

Phalaropes feed on land and water, picking up small insects, crustaceans, worms and molluscs in their long bills. A few seeds are also eaten. Wilson's phalarope feeds more on land than the others and may be beneficial, taking large numbers of crane fly larvae and other pests. All three phalaropes have the strange habit of spinning around in the water like a top, at up to 60 revolutions a minute. This may just be due to the birds continually turning to the rear to snap up food. On the other hand they may, by this spinning, set up a small whirlpool that stirs food up from the bottom of shallow water,

or disturbs small animals, such as mosquito larvae, which can then be easily seen by their movements. Phalaropes also up-end like ducks.

The red phalarope has the peculiar habit of feeding on whale lice, settling on the backs of surfaced whales like a marine version of the oxpecker. During the Arctic summer they feed on the backs of killer whales and belugas and in their winter feeding grounds in the tropics they settle on sperm whales. They also settle on masses of floating seaweed to reach for small animals living among the fronds.

Topsy-turvy courting

Like button quails and painted snipe, the breeding habits of phalaropes are back to front. The brightly coloured and aggressive females display to each other and establish territories from which they court the attention of the dowdy males. Sometimes several females may pursue one male.

Phalaropes breed in colonies, sometimes quite large, with the nests well spread out. Both sexes build the nest which is a hollow lined with grass. The 4, rarely 3, eggs are incubated by the male alone for about 3 weeks. The female remains near the nest and sometimes helps in tending the chicks.

Chemical breeding control

The differences between male and female lie in both form and behaviour, but in phalaropes these differences are reversed. It is, therefore, of interest to examine the underlying causes of the reversal of sexual characters in phalaropes where courtship and incubation roles have changed without any alteration in the basic roles of the sexes in mating and egglaying. Usually the two are intimately linked; a castrated male chicken changes from the aggressive and amorous cockerel to the timid capon, for hormones secreted by the testes and ovaries control the behaviour associated with breeding. In phalaropes the hormones have been reversed. It is usual for each sex to have both male and female hormones, but for females to have very little male hormone and vice versa. The ovaries of the female phalarope, on the other hand, secrete large amounts of androgen, or male hormone. It is this hormone that is responsible for their bright breeding plumage and their aggressiveness. Male phalaropes incubate the eggs and develop brood patches—the areas of bare skin on the breast which keep the eggs warm. Incubation behaviour and brood patches are controlled by the usually female hormone prolactin of which $3\frac{1}{2}$ times more is found in male than in female phalaropes.

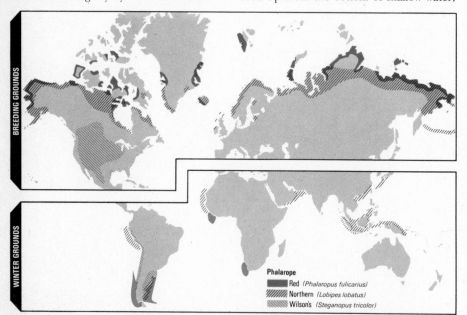

BREEDING GROUNDS

WINTER GROUNDS

Phalarope
■ Red *(Phalaropus fulicarius)*
▨ Northern *(Lobipes lobatus)*
▧ Wilson's *(Steganopus tricolor)*

▽ *Solitary swimmer, a male red-necked or northern phalarope in his winter plumage.*

▷ *Complete contrast hiding among horsetails, a northern phalarope in summer plumage.*

Eric Hosking

class	**Aves**
order	**Charadriiformes**
family	**Phalaropodidae**
genera & species	***Lobipes lobatus*** northern phalarope ***Phalaropus fulicarius*** red or grey phalarope ***Steganopus tricolor*** Wilson's phalarope

Pheasant

The name 'pheasant' comes from the Greek meaning 'the bird from the River Phasis' in the country formerly known as Colchis, to the east of the Black Sea. There are two species of true pheasant but the name has been extended to include monal pheasants, eared pheasants, gallo-pheasants, longtailed pheasants, ruffed pheasants, peacock pheasants and the argus pheasant. These are all large and beautiful birds with long tails, the males being more showy than the females.

The two species of true pheasant are the green pheasant of Japan and the game pheasant, with many subspecies, from the Caucasus to eastern China and Formosa. The cock game pheasant has a brown plumage marked with buff, black and purple, and a long tail barred with black, but the general effect is of burnished copper. The head and neck are dark green, red wattles surround the eyes and there is a pair of earlike tufts on the head. The hen has a brown, duller plumage. The cock pheasant is up to 35 in. long of which 20 in. is tail, the hen being up to 25 in. of which 10 in. is tail. The game pheasant has been naturalised in many countries and the original subspecies has been crossed especially with the Chinese ringnecked pheasant.

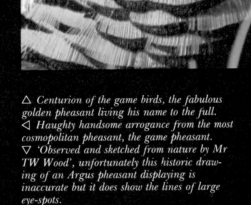

roebild

△ Centurion of the game birds, the fabulous golden pheasant living his name to the full.
◁ Haughty handsome arrogance from the most cosmopolitan pheasant, the game pheasant.
▽ 'Observed and sketched from nature by Mr TW Wood', unfortunately this historic drawing of an Argus pheasant displaying is inaccurate but it does show the lines of large eye-spots.

The three species of monals of the Himalayan region are thickset with short, square tails, the males metallic green, blue, purple and coppery red above, velvety black below. The hens are streaked brown. The 10 species of gallo-pheasants, known as silver pheasants and firebacks, of the Himalayas to Malaysia, have arched tails and velvety wattles on the face. The males are black, blue, purple or white above, black underneath. In the three species of eared pheasants, of China, the sexes are alike. Their plumage is hair-like, the tail is large, there are velvety wattles on the face and long white feathers on the sides of the head. The five species of long-tailed pheasants range from Japan and eastern China to Burma and Thailand. The cock is yellow, coppery red and dark blue marked with black, grey and white. It has red wattles and a long barred tail. The hen is brown marked with black and buff.

The ruffed pheasants include the magnificent golden pheasant and Lady Amherst's pheasant from the mountains of central and western China. The cocks have a crest and a ruff and the plumage is yellow and red in the golden pheasant, green and blue with white in Lady Amherst's pheasant. Peacock pheasants, of the forests from eastern India to Borneo, are small with long tails, grey and brown plumage, marked with metallic green and brown 'eye-spots' and have two spurs on each leg.

A merry band of hen game pheasants tread daintily through the snow. These birds look drab compared with their brilliant male counterpart overleaf.

Fritz Siedel

Unwilling but powerful

Like all pheasants game pheasants are ground birds, feeding and nesting on the ground and roosting in trees. Their wings are short and rounded, and although they do not fly far their flight is strong and fast. If alarmed they run rapidly over the ground, or take off by flying almost straight up, in what looks like a laboured flight. They reach, however, surprisingly high speeds; 60 mph is a figure often mentioned, but whether these are accurate records has yet to be proven. Their legs and toes are strong and spurred, the toes, with strong claws being used in scratching the ground for food: insects, seeds, berries, fallen fruits and leaves, worms, slugs, snails, lizards, even small rodents and young snakes. Roots, bulbs and tubers are also eaten when unearthed.

Driven to distraction

Male pheasants are usually polygamous although there are reports of monogamy when hens are scarce. The cock displays to the hen by blowing up his wattles, puffing up his feathers and parading in front or to the side of her with the wing nearest her drooping and his tail curved towards her. The hen scrapes a shallow depression in the ground and lines it with leaves and grass, usually under coarse grass, bracken or brambles. Some 8–15 olive brown eggs are laid in April and these hatch in 22–27 days, usually being incubated by the hen alone, with the male helping only exceptionally. The young can fly when a fortnight old.

Once called injury feigning, the well-known trick used by a hen pheasant when the nest is in danger is now classed under the general heading of distraction display. When there are chicks in the nest they slip off silently and unobtrusively into the cover of adjacent vegetation and stay still, blending with the background colour. The hen, at the same time—and she will do this also while the eggs are unhatched—runs from the nest, trailing a wing as if injured. A ground predator, such as a fox, follows what looks like a disabled parent who leads him on for up to 100 yd before taking wing and, flying in a wide curve, returning to a point near the nest and disappearing into cover until all is safe.

Sleepyhead beware

In their native home pheasants are killed by the usual birds and beasts of prey and their eggs and chicks taken. When naturalised in foreign countries they are often protected by keepers who kill off any bird or beast that might attack the pheasants or their nests. Domestic cats will wait at dawn for pheasants to come down from their roosts and this is probably the pattern of hunting used by natural ground predators in the pheasants' native home.

An eye for the ladies

The argus pheasant lives deep in the jungles of Malaya, Sumatra and Borneo. The male is 6 ft long, including a long tail and he makes a clearing in the forest on which to display to the female. The secondary flight feathers of his wings are enormously long and each is decorated with a line of large eye-spots—Argus in Greek mythology was a monster with 100 eyes. The argus pheasant is mainly brown and grey but when the male displays he raises the wing feathers to form a huge fan. The bird was made famous by Darwin's account of it in his *Descent of Man*, published in 1871, with an artist's drawing of the pheasant in display. This picture was copied many times in books of the period but was found to be incorrect in detail when David Seth-Smith, then Curator of Birds at the London Zoo, photographed the display in the mid-1920's. The main point is, however, that Seth-Smith's photographs show the pheasant peeping through a space at the angle of the wing for all the world as though he is watching to see what effect his fine feathers are having on the hen.

class	**Aves**
order	**Galliformes**
family	**Phasianidae**
genera & species	**Argusianus argus** *argus pheasant* **Chrysolophus amherstiae** *Lady Amherst's pheasant* **C. pictus** *golden pheasant* **Crossoptilon mantchuricum** *brown eared pheasant* **Lophura spp.** *firebacks and silver pheasants* **Phasianus colchicus** *game pheasant* **Syrmaticus soemmerringi** *copper longtailed pheasant* **S. reevesi** *Reeves longtailed pheasant others*

Phoronid

With their crown of tentacles phoronids are tube-dwelling marine worms which are sometimes taken for one of the many annelid worms because of their similar habits. However, 15 or so species of **Phoronis** and **Phoronopsis** make up a phylum of their own, the Phoronida. The crown of tentacles, covered with cilia and used for collecting food, is known as a lophophore. It is also found in moss animals and lampshells and the three groups are thought to be related, though superficially unlike. The tentacles of phoronids number from 18 to well over 500 according to species and age. They are arranged in a single row along each of two basal ridges that curve together to form a horseshoe or crescent, with the mouth between. Sometimes the two ends of the crescent are spirally rolled increasing the length of the ridge and so the number of tentacles. Below the crown, and marked off from it by a slight groove or by a collar, is the body which is slender and uniformly cylindrical except where it widens at the hindend into a bulb. Though faintly ringed, it is not segmented as in earthworms and other annelids, nor does it bear any appendages. It is muscular and contains a long U-shaped digestive tract lying within a space—the coelom. The digestive tract runs from the mouth down to the expanded far end of the body and back again to an anus just outside the crown of tentacles. This is clearly a good arrangement for a tube-dwelling animal. There is a system of blood vessels containing blood cells that are red, like ours, with haemoglobin. Most species are small, about ¼ in., but one, **Phoronopsis californica**, found on mudflats on the North American west coast, can exceed 12 in. This species has an orange body and bright red tentacles.

Tube dwellers

Phoronids live in shallow waters, down to 180 ft, in tropical and temperate seas. They spend all their time in tubes which they secrete around themselves. These tubes may be calcareous or they may be horny and coated with pieces of stone and shell. The phoronids may occur singly, their lower ends embedded in sand or mud, or they may form tangled masses on rocks and wooden piles. Other species burrow into limestone or the shells of molluscs including the British species *Phoronis hippocrepia. Phoronis australis*, of Australia, India and Japan, is unusual; it entwines its delicate transparent tubes within the material of the tube of another animal, the tube-living sea anemone *Cerianthus.* Often there are 20 or 30 associated with each anemone. This phoronid does little more than push the front end of its body out of the tube and spread its tentacles, then suddenly withdraw it when disturbed. The individual tentacles show little in-dependent movement and small particles of food are caught by water currents set up by the beating of cilia, mostly on the inner side of each tentacle. Water flows in between the two rows of tentacles and out between the bases of the tentacles while food particles are caught in mucus and wafted by the cilia towards the mouth. Inedible particles are rejected as they get near the mouth or are driven to the tentacle tips, against the general current, there to be rejected, the tentacles bending outward in response to their presence.

Unusual powers of regrowth

Though phoronids normally withdraw promptly when disturbed, the crowns of tentacles are nevertheless sometimes bitten off by predators. However, they can be re-grown and it has also been noticed that phoronids kept in aquaria often cast them off by muscular action and regenerate new ones. In one very small species the cast crowns grow new bodies but this is unusual. One species *P. hippocrepia* degenerates in unfavourable weather, in winter off Naples, in summer off Japan, leaving only a few fragments of itself in the tube. When conditions become favourable once more new individuals are formed from these fragments. In a group capable of this amount of regeneration, we can expect asexual reproduction to occur, but this has only been described for one species *Phoronis ovalis* where the animal splits across the middle of the body, to form two individuals, or else gives off buds. In either case, the hind part of the body grows a new crown of tentacles which projects from a new length of tube made at right angles to the old one.

An exquisite actinotrocha larva of **Phoronis** *seen from the side. It is found in the summer plankton feeding on microscopic organisms which are collected by the cilia on the hollow tentacles (×70).*

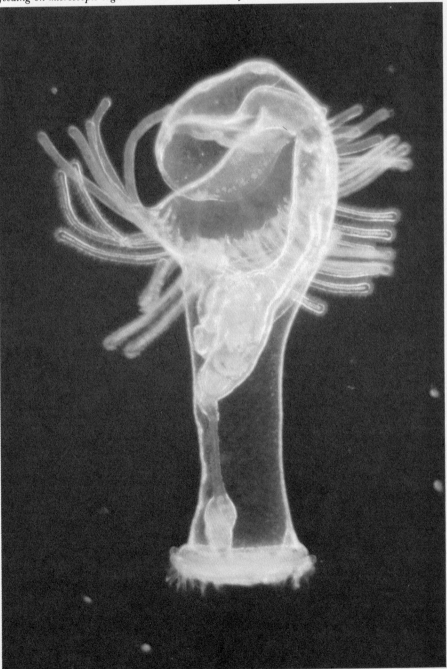

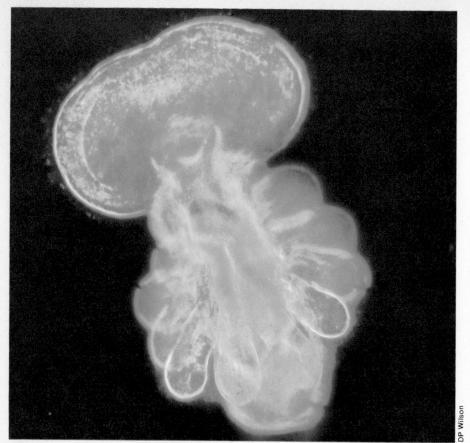

△ *A young actinotrocha larva or* **Phoronis** *seen from below (about × 300).*

▽ **P. psammophila.** *Once out of its sandy tube its feeding tentacles can be seen (× 90).*

DP Wilson

AJ Southward

Different ways with eggs

In the northern hemisphere, phoronids breed mostly in spring and summer. In some species there are separate males and females, but the majority of phoronids are hermaphrodite. When the sex cells are ripe they are released into the body cavity and spawned through the pair of excretory organs. In some species fertilisation occurs while the sex cells are still inside this cavity, and in others only after they have been shed into the water. The eggs may be shed directly into the sea or they may be brooded for a while in the shelter of the tentacular crown. One species is exceptional in plastering its eggs to the inside of its tube or to a nearby rock with a sticky secretion. Eventually the eggs hatch to give rise to planktonic larvae that swim freely by means of cilia, some of which are arranged in a ring at the hindend—the main propulsive organ. Gradually the larvae put out about 6—24 hollow ciliated tentacles. When fully developed these larvae are called 'actinotrochs' and are commonly found in the summer plankton. They may be up to $\frac{1}{5}$ in. and have a large hood bent forward over the mouth. For several weeks, the larvae swim about feeding on microscopic organisms gathered by their cilia, but eventually they become sluggish and sink to the bottom. Then in only 15—30 minutes they undergo a rapid metamorphosis involving convulsive contractions of the body and the eversion of a large pouch to the exterior. This pouch enlarges and becomes the body wall of the trunk. Carried out with it is the middle part of the digestive tract which is thus thrown into the characteristic hairpin loop. The hood over the mouth shrinks and is cast off and eaten along with the larval tentacles, while new tentacles arise from buds. After these drastic changes, the young worm starts to secrete its tube.

Two names, one animal

Phoronids were first known from their larvae, found by Johannes Müller in 1845 in large numbers at the surface of the sea near Heligoland. Thinking they were adult animals, Müller named them *Actinotrocha branchiata*. It was not until 1856 that Dr Strethill Wright of Edinburgh found the adults. He had been sent a stone from Ilfracombe in Devon with a coral growing on it. On it were little worms which Wright named *Phoronis*, from an epithet applied to Io of Greek mythology. He gave them the specific name of *hippocrepia* for the horseshoe shape of their crowns. Wright, however, did not realise he had found the adults of the actinotroch larvae nor was this known until several years later, when the actual metamorphosis was seen. Now according to the International Rules of Zoological Nomenclature when an animal is given two names the earlier, in this case *Actinotrocha*, must be used. *Phoronis* has, however, remained the accepted name in spite of the efforts of some scientists to change it.

phylum	**Phoronida**
genera	*Phoronis*
	Phoronopsis

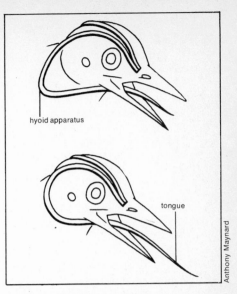

Anthony Maynard

Male white-bellied piculet Picumnus spilogaster. It ranges from Venezuela, Guyana, and Surinam, to Brazil. As shown in the diagram the flexible tongue which 'wipes up' insects is part of an apparatus of bones and elastic tissue, known as the hyoid, and when this apparatus is slipped round the head the tongue is protruded.

Piculet

Piculets are small woodpeckers, between 3 and 5 in. long. In appearance and habits they are more like nuthatches than typical woodpeckers. An important difference is that the tail feathers are not stiff and pointed, so the tail does not have the tattered appearance seen in the true woodpeckers. One toe, however, is turned back in true woodpecker fashion.

There are eight species of piculet. Two live in southeast Asia, one in western and central Africa and the rest in tropical Central and South America and the West Indies. They are generally grey or green above with spotted or streaked underparts. The olivaceous piculet, the only species on the American mainland north of Panama, has olive-green upperparts, throat and upper breast.

The tail is black with a broad stripe of yellow and the belly is yellowish. The top of the head is black with white dots and fine orange streaks in the male only. The Antillean piculet, of Hispaniola and Gonave Island, has greenish upperparts with yellowish white underparts streaked with black. Both sexes have a yellow crown, but the male's has a red centre. The rufous piculet of Malaya is olive green above, rufous below. The forehead of the male is yellow, whereas the female has a rufous forehead.

Acrobatics in the canopy

Piculets hunt in tropical forests by hanging among the fine twigs in the tree canopy, agilely working their way through them and hanging at all angles, like tits. They go about in pairs or small family groups. Sometimes they work on trunks in the manner of nuthatches, but as they lack the stiff tail feathers of woodpeckers they do not press their tails against the trunk as a support while they are hammering.

Hammer-blows for insects

The bill of a piculet is the same shape as that of a true woodpecker but is comparatively smaller and not so sharp. Nevertheless, piculets feed by hammering at wood or searching bark for insects. They cannot drill holes except in the softest wood but they hammer more vigorously than tits or nuthatches, which also search for insects hidden in wood. The olivaceous piculet is very fond of ants and hammers to bring them out. Larvae and pupae are eaten as they are exposed by the damage done by the bill.

Nest drill

Despite their comparatively weak bills, piculets carve out their own nest chambers. The rufous piculet is often found in bamboo jungles and makes its nest chamber simply by boring a hole in a bamboo stem. The olivaceous piculet drills out its chamber, choosing trees that have decayed to almost balsa-wood softness. The nest is built near the ground, not more than about 5 ft up, and is not lined. Both sexes take part in drilling the nest, sometimes working to-gether, exchanging trilling calls as they work. One pair kept under observation took about a week to complete the nest. Afterwards they both slept in the nest at night and by day they took turns to incubate the 2 glossy white eggs. The chicks were naked and blind when they hatched. Their eyes opened at 8 days and the feathers sprouted at 16 days. The parents fed them, mainly on the larvae and pupae of ants.

The chicks leave the nest when 24—25 days old but return to the parents at night for another 3 months. Olivaceous piculets often have to make new nests or sleeping holes because the rotten trees they choose are liable to fall down.

Long tongues

One of the distinguishing features of the woodpeckers, including the piculets, wrynecks and flickers (p 783), is their extraordinarily long tongues, which are used to 'wipe up' or spear insects, often from narrow crevices or holes. The tongue is supported on a long, narrow bone which divides into two horns. This structure is common to all birds, but in the woodpecker family the horns are extremely long. They pass from the base of the lower mandible under the skull, round the back and over the top. In the piculets, and some of the flickers and woodpeckers, the horns stop at the base of the upper mandible, but in other flickers and the wrynecks and woodpeckers they continue into one side of the upper mandible or curl under the right eye. A muscle runs from near the tip of the lower mandible and along the length of the horns. When it contracts the horns are pulled forward and pressed against the skull, so forcing the tongue out. The tongues of piculets are long, but the record is held by the green woodpecker with its 6in. tongue.

class	**Aves**
order	**Piciformes**
family	**Picidae**
genera & species	***Picumnus olivaceus*** olivaceous piculet ***Sasia abnomis*** rufous piculet

Piddock

Piddocks are marine bivalve molluscs that bore into stone, wood, peat and sand with a remarkable rotary action. Their shell is broader at one end than the other. The outer surface at the broad end is toothed like a file and is used for rasping. When in the burrow a pair of long siphons reach up towards its mouth, and if disturbed the piddock discharges a jet of water through these. The siphons are united right up to the tip and are partly covered with the horny material that covers the shell. One siphon draws in a current of water, bringing oxygen and food particles, while the other gives out a waste-carrying current.

Besides having a file-like end the shell must be made to scrape. This is made possible by an unusual arrangement in the hinge. In most piddocks the ligament found in other bivalves has been lost and the hinge teeth reduced to a double ball joint. The latter allows the two valves of the shell to rock on each other in a see-saw movement, by alternate contractions of the two adductor muscles, one in front of and one behind the hinge. In other bivalves these muscles run from valve to valve and contract in unison to close the shell. In the piddock, the adductor muscle nearest the front of the animal is the larger of the two and part of it is spread outside the shell and joins the valves above the hinge. In some piddocks, this exposed muscle is protected by one or more extra plates of shell. At the front of the shell where the foot emerges there is, in most species, a permanent gape. Apart from this region, the flaps of mantle tissue that lay down and line the shell are joined up, so the gills are not visible between the edges of the shell. This almost complete enclosure of the gills within the mantle cavity is common in boring and burrowing bivalves.

The name 'piddock' came into use in the early 18th century but it is not widely used outside Britain. These molluscs are therefore known, in North America for example, as rock-borers, rock-boring clams or merely as pholas, from the scientific name of the best known of them. Wherever they occur they are very similar to the European species. The common piddock, the largest, up to 6 in. long, ranges from southern Britain to Morocco, the Mediterranean and Black Seas. The little piddock, 2½ in. long, makes horizontal rather than vertical burrows. The oval piddock, 3½ in. long, is found all round the northern coasts of Europe as well as the British Isles. The paper piddock is peculiar in that when it has finished burrowing, and is at most 1½ in. long, the gape in the shell through which the foot is pushed out becomes closed off by extensions of the shell, which also becomes trumpet-shaped at the base of the siphons.

△ A boring life. The common piddock, as do all piddocks, bores into rock essentially for protection. The shell is cut away at the front where there is a perpetual gape through which the rounded foot projects. This acts as a sucker, gripping the head of the boring and so anchoring the piddock firmly to the rock.

▷ When the piddock has successfully bored into rock its siphons protrude at the tunnel's entrance. In this photo the outer part of the hole has been cracked away to expose fully the long and united siphons. Their position is shown below in an American rock-borer **Pholadidea loscombiana.**

Heather Angel

MS Laverack

△ *Close-up on piddock holes. The piddock usually continues boring throughout its life. Although safe from enemies in this solitary confinement, there is no escape: as it bores deeper into the rock it grows and makes a wider tunnel so escape back along the narrower, older tunnel is impossible.*

▽ *The shell of the common piddock is elongate, white and rather delicate with up to 50 longitudinal rows of spines where ribs and concentric ridges cross. The extra shell plates which protect the shell-closing adductor muscles are prominent between the valves on the upper surface of the two main shells.*

MS Laverack

Rotary borers

Except in the paper piddock, boring generally continues throughout the piddock's life and, as the animal grows, the inner end of the tunnel becomes wider than the older part bored when the piddock was younger. Needless to say, the piddock cannot leave its burrow. Except in the white piddock, which is more suited to boring in softer materials, the foot ends in a broad sucking disc and, as the valves open, the shell is rotated by the foot muscles alternately one way and the other to make a circular hole.

Mechanism of feeding

Piddocks feed in the same way as other bivalves. Fine particles are sucked in through one siphon and strained from the water by the gills, caught in mucus and passed to the mouth. The water currents and the highly organized streaming of the food particles over the gills, over the sorting areas of the lips (labial palps) to the mouth and even inside the stomach, are all the work of the cilia. Sand and other rejected particles are wafted by cilia into the current in the outgoing siphon where they are joined by faeces and materials from the excretory organs. This current also carries out the sex cells in the breeding season. Little more is known of the breeding habits.

Wasted sparks

Although the production of light is not unusual in the animal kingdom, it is hardly what one would expect of a piddock hidden away in a rock. Yet the common piddock has three pairs of powerful light organs that secrete a luminous slime. Inside the outgoing siphon, and for about two thirds of its length, are two long, thin glandular strips, and there are two triangular glandular patches on the outer sides of the muscles that retract the siphons. The third pair are again long and narrow and run around the inner edge of the mantle so as to partly surround the foot opening. The slime is on occasion shot out of the siphon, its release being under nervous control, but its function is not known, even if something is known of its chemistry. Réamur was the first to discover, in 1793, that the slime could be dried and still be made to give out its greenish blue light on the addition of water. Dried slime can be preserved for a year or more. Dubois studied the matter further in 1897 and discovered that the light is the result of a reaction involving two substances which he called luciferin and luciferase. The luciferin is secreted in granules which luminesce as they dissolve, a reaction which requires oxygen and the presence of the enzyme luciferase, though certain oxygen-supplying chemicals such as potassium permanganate or hydrogen peroxide can be substituted for the latter.

phylum	**Mollusca**
class	**Bivalvia**
order	**Eulamellibranchia**
family	**Pholadidae**
genera & species	*Pholas dactylus* common piddock *Pholadidea loscombiana* paper piddock, others

Peter J Green at Natural History Museum

Pig

Domesticated pigs, or hogs, are derived from two wild species, the European wild boar and the Chinese wild pig. The Indian or crested wild boar may have contributed but this is doubtful. It is not certain whether these three animals represent three different species or whether they are one species ranging across Europe and Asia as far as the East Indian islands, as well as North Africa. The tendency today is to accept the latter idea. One reason for the uncertainty is that the wild pigs in question show a great deal of variety. One that probably must be separated from the rest is the pygmy hog of Nepal which is only 1 ft high at the shoulder.

The Eurasian wild boar—the Chinese and Indian being grouped with it— usually grows to 4 ft head and body length, sometimes up to 6 ft. Its tail may be up to a foot long, and height at the shoulder up to 3 ft. The boar's weight may be up to 420 lb, the sow's up to 330 lb. Its tusks may be a foot in total length, including the continually growing root. The Eurasian wild boar is pale grey to brown or black in colour, the body hairs being sparse bristles with some finer hairs; the tail has only short hairs. Some individuals have longer hairs on the cheeks or a slight mane, or both.

▷ *Food for pigs. In a forest clearing in Germany 250 wild pigs gather for their evening meal, put out for them by the local inhabitants.*
▽ *Bliss! A wild boar wallows in muddy water.*

Fritz Siedel

We-ha

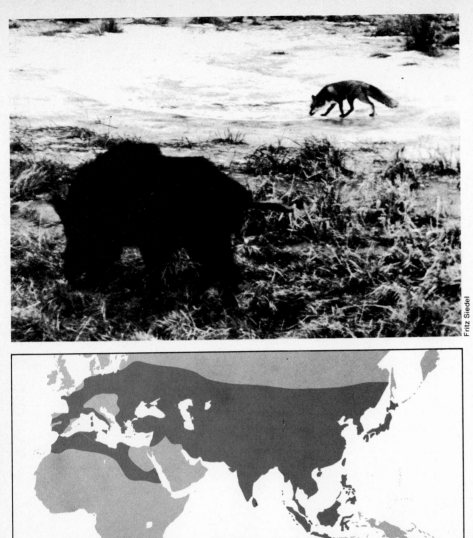

Fritz Siedel

Pig (Sus scrofa)

The family party

The social unit of the pig is usually the family party but in the autumn family groups come together to form bands of up to 50 females and youngsters, the old males mainly remaining solitary. Pigs live mainly in open woodlands, especially where there are mud wallows in which they will spend many hours at a time if undisturbed. They also make crude shelters by cutting long grass then crawling under it to lift it so that it becomes entangled with the tall herbage around to form canopies. Quick footed and good swimmers, pigs normally avoid combat but will act vigorously when provoked, slashing with their tusks.

Nocturnal rootings

Wild pigs may travel far in a night rooting for anything edible. They will eat acorns and beechmast, roots of various kinds, fallen fruits, even the roots of ferns which few other animals eat. They have a natural tendency to dig for the potato-shaped fungi known as truffles. They will also eat insects, lizards, eggs, leverets, fawns, mice, voles, carrion, and any birds they can seize, in fact a very mixed diet. If allowed, they play havoc among cereal crops and root crops such as beet or turnip, and among potatoes. For this reason they have been hunted for centuries, although they have also been hunted for their flesh and for the sport they give.

△ *Two inhabitants of the forest, a boar and a fox, seek food and water on a winter evening.*
▽ *Two wild boar emerge into a forest clearing. The snow makes it harder for them to get food.*

Jean Philippe Varin: Jacana

Fritz Siedel

C Baucher: WWF

△ *The dark form of a wild boar on its way through a white forest.*

△ *A wild boar kicks up its heels and runs. They are not often aggressive.*

Striped young

The sow is in season every 3 weeks and produces litters of 3–12 after a gestation of 112–115 days. She has 8–14 teats and as each piglet takes a teat at feeding time the weaklings in a large litter will die. They suckle for about 12 weeks before being completely weaned onto food which they find while rooting around, never very far from the protection of their mother. The boar takes no part in caring for the young. These young are striped, like other wild pigs. They are sexually mature at 18 months, and reach full size at 5–6 years of age. The pig has a life-span of up to 27 years.

Early domestication

Wild pigs cannot be readily herded but they take well to life in stys or in houses, so we can be fairly sure that their domestication must have come about when men ceased to be hunters and settled down to agriculture. Another clue is in the taboo on eating pig flesh, which seems to have originated in the nomads' contempt for the agrarian communities, expressed in a supposed disgust at the pigs they kept. This was probably reinforced by the disease trichinosis, that could be contracted from

eating insufficiently cooked pork. The earliest domestication date is uncertain but it is unlikely to have been before the Neolithic period, with its agricultural revolution.

The European wild boar is larger than the Chinese pig. They represent extremes of a range in size and the evidence is that pigs were domesticated from local races, so giving domestic pigs of various sizes. There is evidence also that in prehistoric times there was importation of breeds from one part of Eurasia to another as well as some selective breeding. So there was a mixture before modern selective breeding began, making it difficult to trace the lineage of present-day domestic pigs.

The pig has been bred almost solely for its flesh and for its fat. Its bristles have been used to some extent for making brushes and the hide for making sandals and other fancy leather goods. Even the bones may be ground up for bone meal fertilizer. Nevertheless, the domestic pig as a living animal has been put to a variety of uses. It has been used for sacrifices; and for a curious custom among the armies of the Roman period, of swearing an oath on a pig or a piglet. Pigs have at various times been used for pulling carts. They have also been trained to detect truffles, which the owner then dug up. In

Ancient Egypt pigs were used for treading in corn, their sharp hoofs making holes of the correct depth for the seed to germinate. Most surprising of all, they were trained in mediaeval England as pointers and retrievers for illicit hunting, in the New Forest, for example. There commoners were forbidden to keep any but the smallest dogs, capable of passing through King Rufus' Stirrup, an iron stirrup 10½ in. high by 7½ in. across. In southern India, where there lives a primitive tribe whose buffaloes wander into the marshes, an old woman was seen to speak to a pig which 'at once trotted into the marsh, rounded up the buffaloes and herded them to her, like a well-trained collie'.

class	**Mammalia**
order	**Artiodactyla**
family	**Suidae**
genus & species	***Sus cristatus*** *Indian wild boar* ***S. salvanius*** *pygmy hog* ***S. scrofa*** *European wild boar* ***S. vittatus*** *Chinese pig*

▽ *The good life? A fat, pink, domesticated sow feeds her hungry offspring.*

Barnabys

Pigtailed monkey

Pigtails are big monkeys, the largest of
the macaques (p 1365), but distinctive
enough, together with their close relatives,
the longtailed monkeys, to be treated
separately. The male weighs 20—30 lb,
the female 15—20 lb. The coat is buff or
brown, and the distinguishing feature of
the pigtail is the whirl or parting in the
middle of the crown of the head from which
radiates a 'cap' of short, dark brown or
blackish hairs. The hair around the cheeks
is light-coloured and outwardly directed.
The face has a long light brown muzzle
and lighter eyelids. The short thinly-haired
tail, only ⅓ the length of the body, is
carried arched over the back with the tip
resting lightly on the rump.

The liontail is smaller, the males weighing only 15 lb, and in it the distinguishing
features of the pigtail are almost cari-
catured. Its fur is black and there is the
same short-haired cap on the crown as in
the pigtail. The cheek-hairs form a long
grey ruff, and the whitish eyelids are conspicuous against the black face. The tail,
though longer, about half the body length,
is similar to that of the pigtail, and may
be carried arched forwards or backwards.
It, too, is short-haired, but as if to em-
phasise the thinness of the tail hair there
is a tuft at the end. 'Lion-headed' would
be as apt a description for this monkey.

Pigtails live in Burma and Vietnam
south to Malaya, Sumatra and Borneo.
They have been introduced into the
Andaman Islands. Liontails are restricted to a small area in the Western
Ghats of southwest India, at heights of
2 500—4 300 ft, where the trees grow to
70 ft or more. They are rare and still
decreasing, being found recently in only
four hill-ranges: the Nilgiris, Anaimalis,
Cardamoms and around Lake Periyar.

▷ Liontailed monkey

Family portrait. Pigtailed monkeys are almost human at times, and like humans, have a great need for social contact, even if it is only visual. In the wild they live in large troops.

Zoological Society, London

Monkey plant collectors

Pigtails make good laboratory animals, especially for psychological experiments. They are much easier to handle than the more nervous and rather vicious rhesus or crabeaters; they are easy to train and co-operate willingly with the experimenter, thus avoiding the stress that so often mars experiments on the mental abilities of monkeys. Experimenters have been struck by the differences between pigtails and other macaques: they stand boldly, unmoved, with their hands turned outwards, quite un-disturbed provided they have the company of others of their kind. There is none of the bar-shaking or threatening of other monkeys, their size is the only drawback.

In Malaya, pigtails are caught when young and kept with human families, and trained to collect coconuts. They readily obey words of command, are easily tamed, and safe to handle. At a word of command they will climb palms, twist off the coconuts and drop them to the ground. EJH Corner reports that a pet pigtail that he had could dis-criminate between the Malay words *mari* (come), *lari* (run) and *ehari* (search for), and react accordingly. Undoubtedly, as he points out, the accompanying gestures help-ed the monkey to interpret correctly.

When shown its image in a mirror, a pigtail will approach cautiously and touch it, then withdraw, making its characteristic pouting face. This pout, made with lips protruded and pressed together, is a facial expression made only by pigtails and liontails among monkeys: it implies a tendency to flee with conflicting social attraction, and is the equivalent of the lip-smacking gesture of other macaques. Then the pigtail ap-proaches again, puts its arm behind the mirror, and gropes about for the other monkey, his eyes all the while fixed on the image. There is no idea in its mind that the 'other monkey' is itself.

The comparative docility and unflappa-bility of the pigtail have enabled us to see many almost human traits in its behaviour. Its need of social contact is one: a pigtail that has been isolated from others will usually not feed—but can often be persuaded to do so if fed by hand, implying that a human companion is the next best thing to another pigtail. It is often enough for a pigtail just to have sight of another. This counts as 'con-tact', which is often all that can be permitted in the laboratory, as a big male may bully a smaller animal. When undergoing psycho-logical tests, pigtails are more patient and persevering than most other monkeys: rhesus monkeys are more impatient, baboons more destructive. Pigtails show distinct pre-ferences to use one or the other hand for grasping, though some are ambidextrous; they are also right- or left-footed, and even right- or left-eyed—just like man.

Whooping troops

Pigtails and liontails both live in tropical rain-forest, spending more time in the trees than most macaques. They live in large troops: Sugiyama's two liontail troops had 16 and 22 members respectively, while in Malaya Irwin Bernstein found two pigtail troops of 30 and 47 respectively. The troops have overlapping home ranges, about $\frac{1}{4}$ ml in diameter. Each troop contains two or more fully adult males one of which is dominant and leads the troop while another, or a young male, brings up the rear. Some solitary males live in and around the troop areas. When two troops approach one an-other to feed on fruit trees that are in the overlap area of their home ranges, the adult males whoop loudly at each other. The smaller troop usually moves away after a few minutes—fighting has never been seen between troops. A large troop may break into two for some hours before rejoining.

Dissecting nuts

Like other macaques, pigtails and liontails have a varied diet. They eat mainly fruit and leaves, but also nuts, flowers, buds, pith and grubs. They pick nuts apart, meticulously peeling them with both teeth and fingers, before eating them.

Lonely breeding

There is no distinct breeding season. A mating pair is often found far from its troop. A single young is born after 170 days; it has brown hair and a flesh-coloured skin. In one month the skin becomes pale brown and then gradually turns black. The hair of the liontail turns completely black except for the face ruff. Only the 'cap' on the head turns blackish in the pigtail. Baby pigtails are weaned at 8 months. A pigtail lived for $26\frac{1}{2}$ years in Milwaukee zoo.

Survival by cross-breeding

Tigers and leopards may kill pigtails and liontails but man is their only serious predator. Liontails have been heavily over-hunted, and it may be that only 1 000, or even less, still exist. Pigtails are more resili-ent, but even they have suffered at man's hand. In heavily cultivated areas the little crab-eating macaque (see p 1365) often manages to survive, but the larger and more conspicuous pigtail gets shot or otherwise squeezed out. Irwin Bernstein, studying monkeys in Malaya, came across an inter-esting situation in a highly cultivated area. A crabeater troop survived in a forest isolated among the fields, and thrived on crop-raiding; among the crabeaters were two monkeys which were obviously hybrids between crabeaters and pigtails. Quite clear-ly, the pigtails that had inhabited the forest had been almost exterminated, and the one or two survivors had been forced to join a troop of crabeaters with which they freely interbred. Finally they too were killed, and only these hybrids remained to show that pigtails had ever been there at all.

class	**Mammalia** K Tanaka
order	**Primates**
family	**Cercopithecidae**
genus & species	*Macaca nemestrina* pigtailed monkey **M. silenus** liontailed monkey

Summing up the situation. An Asiatic pika **Ochotona hyperborea** *with its small rounded ears flattened back, hesitatingly emerges from its hiding place among the rock crevices. Its main hope of safety lies in remaining hidden from the weasels, small carnivores and hawks that prey on it.*

Pika

Pikas are small mammals related to the rabbits and hares. They are known by a variety of names, including mouse-hares, rock rabbits, rock conies, calling hares, piping hares and whistling hares. There are two species in North America and 12 in Asia; the largest is a foot long, the smallest less than half this. They look like rabbits or hares with short rounded ears, tailless and with the four legs more or less the same length. Each foot has five toes, and the soles of the feet are hairy, enabling them to run easily over smooth rock surfaces. The fur of pikas is usually greyish brown above and lighter on the underparts, but is reddish in one species. In general the coat is lighter coloured in dry areas, darker in more humid regions. Some species have two moults a year giving a summer coat that is reddish or yellowish and a grey winter coat.

The North American pikas live in and around the Rockies, in the Sierra Nevada, Utah and New Mexico and southeastern Alaska and the Yukon in the north. In Asia they range from the Volga and Urals to Korea and the Japanese island of Hokkaido, and in southern Asia from Persia to Nepal.

From lowlands to Mount Everest

One species of pika lives on Mount Everest up to 17 500 ft, the highest altitude at which any mammal has been found. Pikas live in a variety of habitats; on plains, in deserts, in forests and on rocky mountainsides. One of their most noticeable features is their voice which is usually a whistle or a sharp bark, ca-ak, repeated many times. Both calls are remarkably ventriloquial, the body being jerked forwards and upwards at each cry. Pikas rely for safety on remaining hidden, dropping into a crevice and there lying still. Among rocky screes they use the crevices and cavities as shelters, while on the plains they burrow.

Making hay while the sun shines

Pikas usually live in places where the winters are cold but they do not hibernate. Instead they have the remarkable habit of cutting vegetation with their chisel-like teeth, drying it in the sun and storing it for winter fodder. A pika may travel several hundred feet from home to cut herbs and grass, carrying these in its mouth to a chosen spot to dry, adding a fresh layer each day. Some climb into the lower branches of young trees to take young green shoots. In winter bark is sometimes eaten as the pikas tunnel under snow, but the main food even then is the dry fodder. This is stored under an overhanging shelf of rock or under a fallen tree, a single store holding a bushel of hay. Pikas feed in the early morning and late

afternoon. Midday is spent basking. During the day the droppings are small, green and dry. At night they are black and wrapped in a jelly-like layer which keeps them soft and wet. These are swallowed again and kept in the stomach to be mixed with fresh food and redigested, a habit first noticed in rabbits. It has been found that if rabbits are prevented from eating their soft night droppings they will die in about 3 weeks as the droppings are their only source of certain essential vitamins, formed by the activity of bacteria breaking down partly digested plant material in the droppings.

The miners of the Yukon and elsewhere in the western half of North America called the pika the starved rat. Although strictly vegetarian they must, nevertheless, be well fed and far from deserving this nickname. Animals in the north temperate regions can stand up to cold so long as they are well fed. It is not the hard winters that kill but food shortages due to freezing up. Pikas keep going even when the ground is covered with snow, because they have their food stores. They even sun themselves on rocks in temperatures of −17°C/0°F!

Small naked babies

The breeding season is May−September, when each female may have 2 or 3 litters. The gestation period is 30 days and there are 3−5 babies in a litter. Each is born naked and helpless and is put in a nest of dried grass. They weigh 1 oz at birth against

the 1 lb weight of the adults, but reach full size in 6−7 weeks, having been weaned when about a quarter grown. The life span of the pika is 1−3 years and during that time their enemies are weasels and other small carnivores, and hawks.

A modern guinea pig?

Pikas enjoyed a measure of obscurity for a long time, but they now look like emerging to fame as laboratory animals. They were first discovered in North America in about 1828, and the naturalist Thomas Nuttal has left us a record of how he heard, in the Rockies, 'a slender but very distinct bleat, like that of a young kid or goat. But in vain I tried to discover any large animal around me'. Finally he located the little animal 'nothing much larger than a mouse'. Pallas discovered the first pika in Asia in 1769 and although he, and others after him, found species after species in the mountainous parts of Asia and on the steppes, little more was known of them except what they looked like, together with their habit of storing hay and their ventriloquial voice, until about a quarter of a century ago. Since then scientists in the USSR have been paying a lot of attention to them. This is not because they are a nuisance, for they live in out-of-the-way places where they do not clash with man's interests, but because they have all the advantages of the guinea pig as a laboratory animal: they are easy to feed and maintain, inoffensive, and they do not need much room.

class	**Mammalia**
order	**Lagomorpha**
family	**Ochotonidae**
genus & species	***Ochotona pallasi*** *Pallas' pika* **O. princeps** *Rocky Mountain pika* **O. wollastoni** *Mount Everest pika* *others*

△ *One of the many Russian pikas* **Ochotona pusilla** *— a compact, tailless bundle of fur.* ▽ *An all weather animal:* **Ochotona collaris** *in its winter coat.*

Chas J Ott: Photo Res

1722

Pike

The pike, aptly nicknamed the 'freshwater shark', is the fiercest predatory fish in the fresh waters of the northern hemisphere. It and its relatives, the pickerel and muskellunge of North America, are held in awe by some fishermen, contempt by others; to many they present a challenge, backed by the legends of size and ferocity—often very tall stories. The record of the largest pike caught is of a 53lb specimen.

Ambush

Pike live in still and running water, spending most of their time motionless among water plants with which their colours harmonize. The pike usually stay in one place and dart out to ambush their prey. Having the dorsal and anal fins set far back on the body gives great thrust to the tail and rapid acceleration, sending the pike out 20–30 ft to seize prey. A pike detects its prey by sight rather than by smell, at distances of up to 50 ft by day, but is probably warned of its approach by vibrations in the water, for a blind pike can also catch food. A pike can see at night

the pike's teeth. Those on the sides of the lower jaw are strong and stick straight up. They are used for seizing prey. The teeth of the upper jaw are smaller, most numerous in the front, and are curved backwards. The roof of the mouth is bristling with teeth pointing backwards, and these prevent prey slipping out of the mouth. The mouth itself has a wide gape. Sometimes large prey may become jammed in the pike's throat with fatal results for the pike, which cannot get rid of it because of the backwardly directed teeth. Large prey successfully swallowed takes a long time to

Ambush: a northern pike in hiding. It will wait here until prey is near enough for it to dart out rapidly to seize an unsuspecting fish.

The pike—or northern pike, as it is known in North America—is long bodied with a large flat, almost shovel-shaped head with large jaws and large mouth bristling with teeth. Its dorsal and anal fins are set far back. Its colour ranges from olive to dark green with pale yellow spots. It grows up to 4½ ft long and weighs up to 53 lb. The muskellunge of the Great Lakes is very like the pike but has scales on only the upper part of the cheek instead of all over it. It grows to 8 ft long and can weigh up to 110 lb. The grass pickerel, from Nova Scotia to Texas, grows up to 2 ft long, and has dark bands on the flanks. The smaller chain pickerel of the eastern United States grows up to 14 in. long and has a chain-like network of dark markings on the side. The black-spotted pike, which is sometimes called the black-spotted pickerel, lives in eastern Siberia, and very little seems to be known about this fifth member of the family.

as well as by day. Its habit is to lie well down in the water because its eyes are set in the top of the head and look mainly forwards and upwards. It has two sighting grooves running to the tip of the snout. A pike's brain is relatively very small, $\frac{1}{1305}$ of the total body weight, much of this being taken up by the optic lobes. This reflects the little effort the pike needs to make a living.

Gin trap jaws

When very small, pike feed on water fleas, worms and the fry of other fishes. As they grow they take progressively larger fish and are less and less tempted by small prey unless it comes so close they can snap it up without moving. They are almost exclusively fish-eaters, especially of fishes belonging to the carp family Cyprinidae and trout. Large pike will also take other water dwellers such as ducks, moorhens, coots, water voles and frogs. There are many authenticated reports of pike eating prey their own size. This is possible no matter how much it struggles because of

digest, and after a big meal the pike lies inert for a week or more, often near the bottom, taking no notice of prey or the fisherman's bait. A pike can take in large prey because its intestine is more or less straight, its stomach being merely a dilatation of the front part of it.

Unusual digestive juices?

A hungry pike will seize prey of a certain size depending on its own size and usually providing its quarry does not move too slowly, although an angler will catch a pike using stationary dead bait. Pike learn, however, not to go after sticklebacks once they have had experience of their spines. It is sometimes said that the digestive juices of a pike 'are phenomenal', because even hooks are eaten away by its stomach acids. This is, in fact, illusory. When digesting a fish the pike's acidity is high on the surface of the prey, very low inside it, and a pike takes 3–5 days to digest a moderately sized fish. A similar high acidity on the surface of a hook would soon erode it.

High egg wastage

Pike spawn from February to May, the younger individuals spawning first. They are stimulated to spawn by the increasing day length and light intensity. They assemble in shallow water, each female attended by several males. Estimates of the number of eggs laid by each female vary from 40 000 to 500 000, the number depending probably on the size of the female. Many fail to be fertilised because the micropyle, the hole in the egg membrane through which the sperms enter, closes 30–60 seconds after they are laid. At first the eggs are sticky and lie singly on the bottom, later rising just off the bottom. They hatch after 2–3 weeks, the larvae feeding on the remains of the yolk sac for 10 days, before starting to catch their own food. The parents take no care of their eggs or young.

Automatic control of numbers

As pike are at the apex of a food pyramid they probably have few enemies except when very young. There is, however, considerable cannibalism which keeps a proper balance. The more richly a water is stocked with other fish the less the cannibalism; and the end result is that pike are seldom so numerous as to deplete the waters, in which they live, of other fish.

Methuselah pike

Most pike live about 7 years once they have survived the massacre of infancy but they have been known to live 10 years or more and Dr C Tate Regan once asserted that possibly 'fish of sixty or seventy pounds weight are at least as many years old'. There have, however, been many exaggerated claims, like the one, first told by Gesner in 1558, about the famous Emperor's Pike. This pike was supposed to have been caught in a lake in Württemburg in 1497 with a copper ring round its gill region with an inscription saying it had been placed in the lake by the Emperor Frederick II in 1230. So it would have been more than 260 years old. What was not explained was why the ring fitted it so well as pike continue to grow until they die. Had it been put on 260 years before the ring would surely have been a tight fit by 1497.

The pike was said to have been 19 ft long and to weigh 550 lb, and there was a painting of it in the castle of Lautern in Swabia. What appears to be a copy of this still hangs in the British Museum (Natural History). Its skeleton is said to have been preserved in the cathedral in Mannheim. When scientists studied it in the 19th century it was found to have too many vertebrae in its backbone!

class	**Pisces**
order	**Salmoniformes**
family	**Esocidae**
genus & species	**Esox americanus** grass pickerel
	E. lucius northern pike
	E. masquinongy muskellunge
	E. niger chain pickerel
	E. reicherti black spotted pike

◁ *Gin trap jaws: a pike can eat prey its own size with the help of its well appointed dental set.*

Pilchard

Like its relative, the herring, the species, **Sardina pilchardus,** *is highly exploited by man – as a sardine when young and a pilchard when adult. The young fish support an extensive canning industry in France, Spain and Portugal; the adults are best known for the pilchard fishery which formerly flourished off Cornwall. The commercial division into sardine and pilchard arises from the geographical races of the species and the extensive migrations.*

An adult pilchard is a silvery fish, shaped like a herring but a little smaller and slightly fatter, growing up to 10 in. long. Its dorsal fin is slightly forward of the midline of the body instead of more or less at the centre, as in the herring (p 1063). Its scales, also, are larger than those of a herring. Otherwise the two are very alike. As in the herring the scales are deciduous. That is they lie in shallow pockets on the surface and are easily rubbed off.

The pilchard is divided into northern, southern, Moroccan and Mauretanian races. The first may go into the North Sea, as far north as Northumberland, although it rarely goes farther east than Plymouth, in the English Channel. Southwards it ranges to the Cantabrian coast of Spain. The second ranges from Cantabria to Cadiz, the third from Morocco to Rio de Oro on the bulge of Africa, and the fourth, a dwarf race, from Rio de Oro to Dakar in West Africa. There is a Mediterranean subspecies **S. pilchardus sardina.** *The closely related genus* **Sardinops** *has two species with several subspecies:* **S. sagax sagax** *lives off the coasts of Chile and Peru,* **S. sagax melanosticta** *off Japan,* **S. sagax ocellatus** *off South Africa, and* **S. sagax neopilchardus** *off the southern half of Australia and around New Zealand. A second species* **Sardinops caerulea** *lives off the Pacific coast of the United States.*

Tinned shoals

Pilchards live in enormous shoals with the individual fishes arranged in echelon. The shoals are made up of fishes of approximately the same size – that is, in age groups – which is a great convenience to man because they sort themselves out naturally for canning! The shoals swim at differing depths during the day and night since they tend to follow the vertical migrations of plankton. By means of very fine gill-rakers the fish sieve even small diatoms from the water passing into the mouth and throat and out by the gills and pick off large numbers of copepods and other planktonic crustaceans. In summer these form the bulk of their food. There is a good deal of variation in the weight of the fish compared with its length, due to the amount of fat in its body. Pilchard feed most from April to July and again in October, when they are heaviest. From November to February or March they fast, taking at most only a very little food.

Drift-netting

Vast shoals are bound to be preyed upon by many predatory fish and seabirds, but the greatest predator is man. The sardines react to attacks from fish and birds by swimming together and milling around in large tight and compact balls, a defence that would be useless against the drift-nets and seines used by fishermen. For pilchards, for example, the nets are shot at sunset, fastened end to end, with one end attached by a rope to the bows of a boat, nets and boat then drifting with the tide.

Identification by balance

Shakespeare seems to have believed that 'Fools are as like Husbands, as Pilchers (pilchards) are to Herrings'. The standard way of discriminating between a herring, pilchard and sprat is to hold each by its dorsal fin. The herring hangs horizontally because the fin is at the centre of the back. In the pilchard it is nearer the head, so the tail dips, and in the sprat it is nearer the tail, so its nose drops. In fact, herring and pilchard are so alike there has even been talk of their hybridizing, and fishes are caught that look very like hybrids. They have 30 rows of scales along one side of the body and 50 along the other. The explanation is that pilchards have oblique rows of alternately large and small scales. In a normal pilchard the small scales are hidden by the large ones. In the hybrid the scales of one side are all large, while those on the other side are large and small.

class	**Pisces**
order	**Clupeiformes**
family	**Clupeidae**
genus & species	**Sardina pilchardus**

Ben Cropp

◁ *Thousands of pilchards schooling on the Barrier Reef bring order out of confusion as they gather in a clockwise direction into a school. The fish will arrange themselves in echelon and each school consists of fish of approximately the same size.*

The spawning is from April to July when each female lays up to 60 000 large eggs, 20–40 miles from shore, in waters with a temperature of 10–17°C/50–63°F. The eggs are peculiar in having a large space between the egg itself and the outer membrane. This, with the large globule of oil each contains, makes the eggs buoyant and they float at the surface. The larvae hatch in 3 days or so, each being ½ in. long.

The temperature needed for spawning differs for each race of pilchard but lies between the limits already quoted. In the northern race there are two distinct populations. One spawns south of Cornwall, sometimes in the English Channel as far east as Dover, or off the coast of Brittany, the young fishes then migrating south to the level of St Jean-de-Luz where they stay for 2 years before migrating northwards to spawn on the grounds where they were hatched. They are fished as sardines off the west coast of France and the north coast of Spain, and as pilchards off Cornwall. The second population spawns in the Bay of Biscay, the young fish from these eggs spending their first 2 years in the same place, after which they migrate north as mature fish (pilchards) and do not return to their birthplace.

In the southern race the young fish, 2 years of age or less, are found off Portugal, the 2–6 year olds being found off the north coast of Spain. In the Moroccan race the young are found off Agadir and the adults off Safi.

Spawning and post-spawning migrations take place from November to June from Gibraltar to Galicia, from November to April from Santander in Spain to Areachon in France, from February to July off Brittany and from April to November in the Celtic Sea—the area west and southwest of Cornwall. The appearance from south to north of shoals of adults following the successive spawning periods gave rise to the idea that there was an extensive south-north migration, whereas it is only a succession of small migrations of local populations.

▽ The unassuming pilchard is an important source of food especially in Spain and Portugal. Like the herring it has soft-rayed fins, and the scales along the belly are easily rubbed off.

Series by DP Wilson

From egg to fish: the fertilised egg and oil globule are enclosed in a delicate capsule. Part of the egg develops into the embryo, the remainder into the yolk sac which serves as a food store for the developing embryo (× 40).

At a later stage the embryo shows clearly the segmented body muscles, head and tail regions. When it hatches out the larval pilchard floats upside-down in the plankton because of the single oil globule in the yolk sac (× 30).

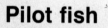

Shark's jackal? Pilot fishes swim alongside a whitetip shark **Carcharhinus longimanus.** *It was believed that pilot fishes guided sharks and rays towards suitable prey, receiving in return protection from enemies because of their closeness to a formidable companion. In reality, however, both fishes are in search of food, the pilot no doubt benefiting from the efforts of its big companion but never leading the foray.*

Fatal shelter

So little is known for certain about the way of life of pilot fishes, and what is known seems extraordinary. It is always supposed that by swimming under the bells of jellyfishes or among the tentacles the baby pilot fishes are protected from enemies. This may be true but they are also exposed to the dangers of being eaten by animals which feed on jellyfishes. These are more numerous than one would think. They include seabirds, such as frigate birds and fulmars and the large fishes, including the large ocean sunfishes. Indeed, there must be the suspicion that these animals may be taking the jellyfishes more for the fishes sheltering under them since jellyfishes are 99% water.

Why follow sharks?

There is also uncertainty about the protection a pilot fish gets from swimming near a shark. It is usually taken for granted that it does get protection because the shark itself is so voracious that potential enemies are unlikely to come near, but a pilot fish would get no protection from swimming with a whale or a shoal of tunny, less still from a bunch of Sargasso weed, a piece of floating wreckage or a sailing ship. We know that pilot fishes sometimes travel inside the mouths of large rays which do not eat fish. It may be they sometimes enter the mouths of sharks—but do not live to serve as evidence! All the signs are that pilot fishes have the instinct to swim near a body larger than themselves; when young it is a jellyfish, when adult it is anything from a shark to a schooner. The very early idea that they are friendly to man is not far from the truth if by being friendly we mean they like to keep close to us—or to our ships.

The researches of the Soviet scientist VV Shuleikin, published about 1957, give the only valid reason for pilot fishes swimming beside sharks and ships. Shuleikin calculated that sharks swim three times as fast as a pilot fish possibly can. How then does a pilot fish keep up? Over the surface of any body moving through water there is a 'boundary layer' of water moving forward at almost the same speed as that of the body. This is thickest over the tail half of a shark, which is where a pilot fish usually swims. So presumably the pilot fish is able to travel hundreds of miles in a boundary layer carried along by it, with a minimum of effort.

class	**Pisces**
order	**Perciformes**
family	**Carangidae**
genus & species	*Naucrates ductor*

Pilot fish

The pilot fish is so named because it was believed to guide sharks and whales, and to lead ships or solitary swimmers to land or to a port when they had lost their way. These beliefs go back at least to the time of the Ancient Greeks.

The pilot fish can grow up to 2 ft long. It has a strongly forked tail that is blackish with white tips, a prominent dorsal fin with 4 strong spines in front of it, a prominent anal fin and small pectoral and pelvic fins. Its body is marked with 5—7 dark bands, brownish to black, on a background of white to bluish-white. It is widespread through tropical and temperate seas and is occasionally caught off the coasts of the British Isles.

Social hangers-on

So far as one can tell, pilot fish do nothing else than swim about in company with large sharks, whales, giant mantas, large schools of tunny and sailing ships. They have sometimes been caught in mackerel and herring nets. Although the ancient belief is that they lead, and therefore guide or act as pilots, they more commonly swim at the side or even follow other fish. Nevertheless, the association is a very persistent one. Pilot fishes accompanying a shark which is then hooked and hauled on board ship have swum around its tail, the last part of the shark to leave the water, as if distracted. Again, a pilot fish is recorded as following a sailing ship continuously for 80 days. The idea that they piloted a ship to port was fostered to some extent by the way the fish

left it as it neared land or after it had entered harbour. One explanation for this, which does not seem unreasonable, is that they turn away when they feel the freshwater brought down by rivers.

Why pilot fishes should accompany large animals and other objects is something of a mystery. One explanation put forward is that, with their better eyesight, they see food before the shark does and lead it to it, taking the scraps as the shark feeds. This is, however, almost entirely guesswork dating at least from the 16th century when pilot fishes were called the sharks' jackals. What seems more certain is that a pilot fish may suddenly dart from a shark's side to snap up something, but it quickly returns to take up station once more. On the few occasions that pilot fishes have been caught and their stomachs examined they seem to have been eating small fishes rather than scraps of food.

Different babies

Spawning seems to take place in the early summer well away from land. It is always said that the eggs float at or near the surface but a note from the Soviet scientist AI Svetovidov, published in 1958, says that pilot fishes always lay their eggs on the skin of sharks or the submerged hulls of ships. The parents then stay with the eggs until they hatch. The larvae hatching from them are so unlike the parent that they were originally thought to belong to a separate species. They have large eyes and numerous spines on the head, and they shelter under the bells of jellyfishes and among the tentacles of the Portuguese man-o'-war, under bunches of Sargasso weed and pieces of floating wreckage.

Pilot whale

*Also called the blackfish or caa'ing whale, the pilot whale is a dolphin that can grow to 28 ft long. Its most distinctive feature, from which it gets its scientific name of **Globicephala**, is the bulging forehead, which forms a dome overhanging the mouth. The upward curve of the mouth gives it an amused look. The tapered flippers are long, about ⅕ of the total body length. The dorsal fin stands about 1 ft high. Pilot whales are black except for a white patch under the chin.*

*Pilot whales are found in many parts of the world but are absent from the polar seas. **Globicephala melaena** of the North Atlantic and Mediterranean ranges as far north as Greenland. It is common off the Faeroes, Shetland and Orkney. **G. macrorhyncha** is found in the Caribbean and off the southeast seaboard of the United States. **G. scammoni** lives in the Pacific Ocean. The last two species have shorter fins than **G. melaena**.*

Mass suicide

Pilot whales live in large schools sometimes numbering hundreds, or even thousands. Each school is made up of both males and females and it has often been reported that a male acts as a leader. This is presumably how these animals got their name, but it is more likely that there is a general tendency to follow any individual. Hunters have found that when one pilot whale is wounded and rushes away, the other members of the school follow it. A dolphin named Pelorus Jack, that regularly followed ships plying between Wellington and Nelson, New Zealand, for 20 years, may have been a pilot whale exhibiting its following habit. On the other hand, some writers think that Pelorus Jack, who had the distinction of worldwide fame and protection under Order in Council, was a Risso's dolphin *Grampus griseus*. The habit of following a leader has, however, made schools of pilot whales very susceptible to become stranded. If one whale, perhaps becoming panic-stricken at finding itself in shallow water, goes ashore, the others follow like sheep. Attempts have sometimes been made to refloat stranded pilot whales, but they have failed. As soon as one whale is dragged into deeper water, it swims back to the shore. Presumably the rescued whales are blindly answering the calls of the stranded ones. Killer whales behave in the same way.

△ *Letting off steam? A Pacific pilot whale* **Globicephala scammoni** *surfaces, 'blowing its nose' as it breathes out. The whale's spout is not water. Whales can submerge for more than half an hour and can tolerate an increase of carbon-dioxide in the blood during this time. Previous page: Follow-the-leader; a school of pilot whales, identified by high dorsal fins.*

Blind hunting

Pilot whales are armed with 7–11 teeth in each side of each jaw. These are used for grabbing slippery prey, which is mainly squid and cuttlefish, but fish are also taken. The eyesight of pilot whales is not good and their bulbous heads and inflexible necks must prevent them from seeing objects directly ahead, so perhaps they use sound waves to find food like other dolphins.

Warm water breeding

Sightings of pilot whale schools over many years show that they migrate regularly. The migrations are partly regulated by food supply, as when pilot whales move to the coast of Newfoundland in summer after the squid *Illex*, but there is a more general movement to warmer waters in winter. It appears that mating takes place in the warmer waters and calves are born when the pilot whales return to cooler regions in the following year.

It is usual for whales to migrate to warmer seas to breed, as does the blue whale (p 248) for instance, for newborn whales have very little insulating blubber. To compensate for this the whale's milk is extremely rich, having only 40–50% water, half as much as cow's milk. The fat content of whale's milk is very high 40–50%, that of cows is only about 4%.

Until observations were made in oceanaria, very little was known about the mating habits of whales, but pilot whales had been seen courting in the wild. The partners have been seen stroking each other with their flippers or bodies as they swim slowly past and on one occasion the mate of a weather ship watched the amorous antics of about 20 pilot whales. They were swimming side by side in pairs, playfully biting each other's mouths, and surfacing vertically until their flippers were exposed. They would then submerge and lie belly to belly for about 20 seconds, copulation in whales being extremely rapid.

Female pilot whales start to breed when 6 years old and bear young in alternate years. They are barren at 18 years. Males mature in 13 years. Pilot whales are thought to live for a maximum of about 50 years.

Orgy of slaughter

For hundreds of years pilot whales have been hunted in the islands to the north of the British Isles. The hunts, which are still carried on in the Faeroes, but have ceased in Orkney and Shetland, depend on a school of pilot whales being sighted near the shore. The alarm is given and a fleet of small boats puts out to carefully shepherd the school into a bay. The whales panic and rush into the shallows. Men from the boats and those waiting on the shore immediately set on the whales with knives and lances.

When the slaughter is over the carcases are stripped of their blubber. The division of the spoils follows a strict tradition. Certain proportions are awarded to the man who first spotted the whales, those who went out in the boats, the men who helped in the slaughter and so on. A share is also put aside for the poor. The capture of a school of pilot whales, was an absolute windfall to the islanders, and even now there are wild scenes following the slaughter of *grindehval*, as the Faeroese call them.

class	**Mammalia**
order	**Cetacea**
family	**Delphinidae**
genus & species	***Globicephala melaena*** *others*

John Tashjian at Marineland of the Pacific

1730

Pink-footed goose

The pink-footed goose is a small variety of the bean goose. The latter is so-named because it arrives in England in October, at the time of the bean harvest and then stays to feed on the beans left lying in the fields. There are two basic types of bean goose; the forest bean geese have long, slender bills, while the tundra bean geese, stockier birds, have shorter deeper bills. The pink-footed geese are the latter type. Their length from bill to tail is 24-30 in. The head and neck are dark brown, the underparts light pinkish brown and the wings and tail ash grey with white edgings. The feet are pink and so is the bill except the base and tip, although it may very occasionally be wholly pink.

Bean geese breed in the tundra and forest zones, from Greenland to eastern Siberia, but the pink-footed goose is restricted to eastern Greenland, Iceland and Spitzbergen. In the winter they migrate to Britain, northern France, Belgium, Holland and Germany. They occasionally turn up in North America, Russia and other parts of Europe.

Wary geese

During the winter pink-footed geese gather in very large flocks on sandbanks, moors, in estuaries, flooded marshes and around coasts—all places where they are unlikely to be disturbed. As is usual with geese, pink-foots are extremely wary and difficult to approach. Pink-footed geese arrive in their winter quarters in September and October, having migrated from the breeding grounds, with only a few stops, in the Faeroes or Scandinavia. They fly in skeins of over 1 000 geese with family parties of adults and goslings keeping together. When they arrive, weary and hungry, they are less

▽ *Pink-footed goose in profile.*

wary than usual and for a few days it is possible to get nearer to them before they recover their strength. The flocks stay south until April or May.

Grazing and gleaning

In the autumn and winter pink-footed geese feed in stubble fields, usually of barley, but they also eat young wheat and grass stems. On the breeding grounds they eat buds, stalks, seeds and leaves of many plants including willow, sedge, horsetails, chickweed and grasses.

Safe nesting places

By the time the pink-footed geese have reached the breeding grounds they have already paired off. All arrive within a few days and only a few more days elapse before the eggs are laid. Most pairs nest in loose colonies but some raise their broods singly, especially in the open tundra. If large numbers nested together in open country predators such as Arctic foxes would be attracted to such easy prey with devastating

results. The colonies are usually in more inaccessible places such as the talus, the piles of boulders that form at the bottom of cliffs, on moraines, cliff ledges or terraces. Some colonies are on islands in rivers. When on level ground the nests are built on hillocks or frost mounds where the sitting bird can get a good view of the surrounding country. The gander usually keeps a watch from a lookout point nearby.

The nest is a depression in the ground lined with grasses and other plants and with a considerable quantity of down. The 4—5 eggs, sometimes more, are incubated by the goose alone while the gander stands guard. The eggs hatch in just under 4 weeks. The chicks leave the nest within 48 hours and never return. Their parents lead them down to water when they leave the nest and a new roost is used each night.

The adults moult during the breeding season, shedding all their feathers simultaneously so they cannot fly until the new ones regrow. As soon as they and their young can fly, they migrate south.

Moments of danger

When they have moulted their flight feathers they are helpless and although the natural wariness of geese usually keeps them relatively safe from enemies, unless they are in an isolated place they will fall prey to Arctic foxes. Greater black-backed gulls, Iceland falcons, white-tailed eagles and Arctic foxes are also known to prey on the eggs and chicks of pink-footed geese in Iceland.

Goose round up

The Arctic breeding grounds of pink-footed geese are a comparatively recent discovery. The birds were first discovered breeding in Spitzbergen in 1855 and in Greenland in 1891. The colonies there were fairly small and many years passed before the main colonies in Iceland were discovered. The first clues came in 1921, but proof was obtained in 1951 when Peter Scott, James Fisher and Finnur Gudmundson travelled to the interior of Iceland and found over

2 000 nests at an oasis on a high plain. They ringed over 1 000 pink-footed geese to find where they spent the winter, catching them by driving them into nets. At that time of the year neither adults nor goslings could fly so they were easy to capture. Nearby they found the remains of U-shaped stone walls 36 ft long and 6 ft across the entrance. These were the ruins of goose pens that had been used by the Icelanders centuries before for rounding up flightless geese. Of course their purpose in capturing them was not for the study of the birds or their migration but to fill up their larders.

class	**Aves**
order	**Anseriformes**
family	**Anatidae**
genus & species	*Anser fabalis brachyrhynchus*

▽ *Winter feeding-grounds—pink-footed geese graze the stubble on a field in northern Europe.*

Pintail

The pintail is probably the most numerous duck in the world. It is the same length as a mallard, 22 in., except that the central pair of tail feathers are elongated, forming the pin-tail which may be as much as 4 in. long in males. The plumage of the male is distinctive, with a blackish-brown head and neck, and with a white collar running down the side of the neck and across the breast. The back and belly are patterned and there is a patch of white on the belly in front of a patch of black at the base of the tail. The female is very much like a mallard duck. The male goes into eclipse from mid-July to early September. The eclipse plumage is like that of the female but is darker on the upper parts and the 'speculum' of bronzy-green with a buff bar on the front, can be seen on the wings.

The pintail is distributed around the northern hemisphere and it migrates south in winter.

The Bahama pintail ranges from the Bahamas through most of South America and also breeds on the Galapagos islands. It has distinctive white patches on the sides of its face. Some pintails breed farther south than any other duck. There are subspecies of the northern pintail on the sub-Antarctic islands of Kerguelen and the Crozets, and South Georgia has its own separate species. These sub-Antarctic pintails are confusingly called teal; and, to add to the confusion, the males are in eclipse plumage all the year round.

Habitat destroyed

The vast inhospitable wastes of the Arctic tundra provide the breeding ground for the pintail which nests in the numerous scattered pools and lakes. Freshwater pools are preferred to brackish ones, and nests are not usually found on water surrounded by marshy ground. In the Galapagos there are very few stretches of freshwater where the Bahama pintail can live. A few years ago a large lake in a volcanic crater on the island of Fernandina was destroyed by an eruption, so robbing the Galapagos pintail population of most of their habitat. In Europe pintail prefer wintering around coasts and estuaries, whilst in India large numbers are found on inland lakes. This is unusual as pintail are usually seen in only small numbers on inland waters. On the sea, however, they may form flocks of over 1 000, these large flocks being split up into small parties which mingle with other ducks rather than forming tightly-packed rafts.

Rarely dive

Pintail feed by paddling in the shallows, upending, or by uprooting water plants such as pond weed, sedge and dock. Acorns and grain from stubble, beetles, fly larvae, worms

▷ *Pintail silhouettes.*

Arthur Christiansen

and tadpoles are also taken. Their winter diet includes seaweed and eelgrass. Pintail do not dive except to escape danger when unable to fly while moulting during eclipse or because of wounds.

Female distractions

The display courtship of the pintail is similar to that of the mallard (p 1382) and there are aerial pursuits in which the female is chased by several males. Pintail often perform aerial dives, plunging at an angle of 45° from a great height, stooping with their wings stiffly outspread and slightly curved down. Just before hitting the ground they level out and glide a few yards off the ground for 100–300 yd.

The greatest concentrations of breeding pintails are probably in the tundra of Alaska where every small pool houses one or more pairs. Elsewhere the nests are fairly close together, sometimes a long way from water. These are no more than a down-lined hollow in the ground among marram grass, heather, rushes or other low plants. The 7–9 eggs are incubated by the female, and usually guarded by the male. The chicks

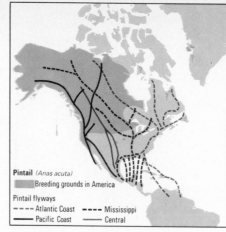

Pintail *(Anas acuta)*
Breeding grounds in America

Pintail flyways
---- Atlantic Coast   ---- Mississippi
—— Pacific Coast   —— Central

△ *Pintail breed throughout the northern hemisphere in Asia, northern Europe, including Britain, Iceland and central and western Canada.*

▽ *Sitting duck. A female pintail on her nest, a down-lined hollow in the grass. The favourite pintail breeding grounds are in the Arctic tundra, around the many scattered pools.*

Eric Hosking

P Morris

hatch out after 22–23 days and shortly afterwards are led to the nearest water to feed. If disturbed, the chicks hide among water plants, and there are records of their mother performing distraction displays in which she approaches close to the intruder, and splashes about vigorously, swimming in circles. The young fly when 5–7 weeks old.

Aerial highways

Ducks of the genus *Anas*, to which the pintail and mallard belong, make up three-quarters of the quarry of wildfowlers. In the United States in particular, vast numbers of wildfowl are shot every year as they fly across the country to and from the breeding grounds in the north. To protect the waterfowl there are stringent game laws and conservation agencies prepare suitable stretches of water for the birds to settle. Their task is made easier because the waterfowl, as well as other birds, travel along traditional routes.

Migrating birds usually take the line of least resistance. Birds of prey, for instance, cross the Mediterranean by the shortest sea routes, over the Straits of Gibraltar and the Bosphorus. Sometimes, however, the only way is over difficult ground. Pintails migrating in and out of India have to cross mountains, and the skeleton of one was found 16 000 ft up Mount Everest. In North America there are four well-defined migration routes that follow geographical features. These were discovered, and named 'flyways' by Frederick Lincoln, from information gathered from banded birds, mainly waterfowl of various species.

The flyways start in the tundra of Alaska and northern Canada, and continue down through the plains of Canada and into the USA. On the way, the ducks and geese from the Arctic are joined by hosts of other birds and finish on winter grounds around the Caribbean Sea or in South America. The most important flyway is that down the Mississippi Valley to the marshy shores of the Gulf of Mexico. Next in importance is the central flyway, also starting in Alaska but then running close to the eastern side of the Rocky Mountains. Along the coasts there are the Atlantic and Pacific flyways, one leading to the West Indies and South America, the other to the Pacific coast of Mexico and California. These flyways are less used because the winter climate of the coasts is less severe than in the centre of the continent. Therefore there is less pressure on the birds to travel south.

class	**Aves**
order	**Anseriformes**
family	**Anatidae**
genus & species	*Anas acuta* pintail *A.* **bahamensis** *Bahama pintail* *A.* **georgicus** *South Georgia pintail*

◁ *Surface feeder: pintail drake dips its bill. They sometimes upend and they often uproot water plants. The two elongated central tail feathers form its distinctive pintail.*

Pipefish

These eel-like fishes were given their name in the mid-18th century, when pipe stems were long and very thin. Today they would probably have been called pipe-cleaner fish. The shape of the body has led to such names as worm pipefish, snake pipefish and threadfish. There are over 150 species from 1 to 18 in. long, in tropical and temperate seas. All are long and very slender with long heads, tubular mouths and tufted gills. Instead of scales, they have a series of jointed bonelike rings encircling the body, from behind the head to the tip of the tail. Some have a small tailfin, in others there is none. The main fin is in the middle of the back.

The colours of pipefishes are usually dull: greenish or olive, like the seaweeds among which they live. Most have a slight banded pattern, which is particularly well marked in the banded pipefish

△ *Pipefish portrait:* **Syngnathus** *shows off its intricate patterning. They often swim in a strange semivertical position with their pectoral fins vibrating so rapidly as to be almost a blur.*

▽ *A group of banded pipefish* **Dunckerocampus caulleryi** *patrol a coral reef off New Caledonia in the South Pacific.*

of New Caledonia. Some are mottled and spotted. Some pipefishes can change colour, like the Florida pipefish, which is normally dark green when among eelgrass but goes light when among pale green weed. Others in American seas are muddy brown but turn brick-red when among red weeds. The sea dragon of Australian coasts has leaf-like flaps and spines, and it looks like a piece of floating seaweed.

Most pipefishes are marine or estuarine and a few are freshwater. The marine species live chiefly inshore, in shallow seas, but some live at depths of 50 ft or more, and one lives among the weed of the Sargasso Sea, off the coast of Florida.

Vertical swimmers

Pipefishes in shallow waters and estuaries often live among eelgrass, the only flowering plant in the sea, with long swordlike leaves. They swim in a vertical position with the dorsal and pectoral fins vibrating in time with each other, driving the fish through the water in a leisurely fashion. The vibra-

tions of the dorsal fin are so rapid as to give the impression of a tiny propeller. They can also slip through the water with snake-like movements of the body. They can turn their heads from side to side, and use these movements for steering. The eyes can be moved independently of each other, as in chameleons. Pipefishes may also be found among seaweeds, at times in rockpools, in holes and crevices, and there are species in tropical seas that live in the interstices in coral rock rubble, almost like earthworms.

Fussy vacuum cleaner

Pipefishes have no teeth and they have been described as suffering from permanent lock-jaw, with the locked jaws supporting the tubular mouth. They cannot pursue prey but do the next best thing. The mouth acts as a syringe and can suck in a small plank-tonic animal from 1½ in. away. When searching for food they may swim upright or in a horizontal position, wriggling and twisting the body, turning the head this side and that and thrusting among tufts of weed or into cracks and crevices. They seem to be selective, apparently scrutinizing each cope-pod or other small animal, tasting the morsel, and ejecting it forcibly if not satisfied. Some spiny larvae of crabs are inspected but left severely alone.

Sexes swap jobs

The main interest of pipefishes is in their breeding. They are related to sea-horses, the males of which have a pouch in which the female lays her eggs. The pipefishes are less simple. In some species the female merely lays her eggs on the underside of the male and there they stick. At the other extreme are species in which the male has a long pouch formed by folds of the surface growing down and meeting in the middle line. There are grades between the two; in some species there are merely two folds of skin in which the eggs lie. All pipefishes have, however, one thing in common: the male carries the burden of the offspring. In many of them the female does all or most of the courting.

Courtship has been fully studied in the Florida pipefish. The two swim round each other in the vertical position but with the head and front part of the body bent forward. They swim in decreasing circles until their bodies touch, when the male bends farther forwards and caresses the female with his snout. He becomes excited, wriggling his body in corkscrew fashion as he continues to caress the female with his snout. Finally, their bodies become entwined, she inserts her ovipositor into his pouch and lays some eggs. The male wriggles his body to work the eggs down into the pouch, after which the female lays more eggs, and this is repeated until the pouch is full. The eggs hatch and the larvae are shot out, one or a few at a time, by the male making convulsive movements. Even when able to swim freely the baby pipefishes may dive back into the pouch in times of danger.

Submarine flirtation

It is not surprising that for a long time the male pipefish should have been mistaken for the female. It was not until 1831 that this

△ *Moment of birth for a father! In some pipefish the male carries the developing eggs in a pouch, the female inserting them as the climax to an intimate caressing courtship.*
▽ *Some* **Syngnathus griseolineata** *have pregnant pouches seen halfway along their bodies.*

RH Noailles: Jacana

was corrected, and it was many years later before they had been studied sufficiently to show how completely the roles of male and female were reversed, even to the female doing the courting. The female broadnosed pipefish of the Mediterranean, for example, courts the male for several hours before he responds. Then he swings his body from side to side, through a right angle, reminding one of the wriggling and swaying of the bashful suitor. This facetious idea receives support from the further behaviour of the female of this species who seems to flirt preposterously, courting one male after another, even mating with several in turn.

class	**Pisces**
order	**Gasterosteiformes**
family	**Syngnathidae**
genera & species	**Nerophis aequoreus** *snake pipefish* **Phycodurus eques** *sea dragon* **Syngnathus acus** *great pipefish* **S. floridae** *Florida pipefish* **S. typhle** *broadnosed pipefish others*

John Tashjian at Steinhart Aquarium